Flash
Pocketbook

GCSE Mathematics Higher Tier

Philip Allan Updates, an imprint of Hodder Education, an Hachette UK company, Market Place, Deddington, Oxfordshire OX15 0SE

Orders

Bookpoint Ltd, 130 Milton Park, Abingdon, Oxfordshire OX14 4SB
tel: 01235 827720 fax: 01235 400454 e-mail: uk.orders@bookpoint.co.uk

Lines are open 9.00 a.m.–5.00 p.m., Monday to Saturday, with a 24-hour message answering service. You can also order through our website: www.philipallan.co.uk

ISBN 978-1-84489-711-7

Impression number 5 4 3 2 1
Year 2015 2014 2013 2012 2011 2010

Printed in Spain

Hachette UK's policy is to use papers that are natural, renewable and recyclable products and made from wood grown in sustainable forests. The logging and manufacturing processes are expected to conform to the environmental regulations of the country of origin.

P01730

Shape, space and measures

Handling data

Types of number

Q1 From the list 1, 2, 3, 4, 5, 6, 8, 12, 16, 18, 19 find:

(a) four prime numbers

(b) three factors of 6

(c) three multiples of 6

(d) all the square numbers

Q2 (a) Find the prime factorisation of 42.

(b) Given that the prime factorisation of 28 is $2^2 \times 7$, find:

(i) the lowest common multiple (LCM) of 28 and 42

(ii) the highest common factor (HCF) of 28 and 42

ANSWERS

A1 (a) A prime number is a whole number that is divisible by 1 and itself only, so from the given list 2, 3, 5 and 19 are prime.

(b) Factors are numbers that divide evenly into the given number; here 1, 2, 3 and 6 are factors of 6 — you can give any three of these as your answer.

(c) Multiples are what you get when you multiply a given number by 1, 2, 3 etc. The multiples of 6 in the list are 6, 12 and 18.

(d) Square numbers are 1, 4, 9, 16, 25 etc. The ones that appear in the list are 1, 4 and 16.

A2 (a) The prime factorisation of 42 is $2 \times 3 \times 7$

(b) (i) The LCM of 28 and 42 is $2^2 \times 3 \times 7 = 84$

(ii) The HCF of 28 and 42 is $2 \times 7 = 14$

examiner's note Remember that 1 is not considered to be a prime number.

Directed numbers

Q1 Calculate:

(a) $7 - (-2)$

(b) $5 - 9$

(c) $-3 - 5$

(d) $-2 - (-8)$

Q2 Calculate:

(a) $7 \times (-3)$

(b) $-28 \div 4$

(c) $(-8) \times (-6)^2 \div 3$

ANSWERS

A1 (a) $7 - (-2) = 7 + 2 = 9$

(b) $5 - 9 = -4$

(c) $-3 - 5 = -8$

(d) $-2 - (-8) = -2 + 8 = 6$

A2 (a) $7 \times (-3) = -21$

(b) $-28 \div 4 = -7$

(c) $(-8) \times (-6)^2 \div 3 = -(8 \times 6 \times 6 \div 3) = -96$

The overall sign is negative because there are three negatives in the product.

***examiner's* note** When multiplying or dividing negative numbers, determine the sign of the answer before you start working out the value.

BODMAS

Q1 Calculate $20 - 6 \times 2 \div 4$

Q2 Calculate $\dfrac{15-(4+3)^2}{3-5}$

Q3 Calculate $24 - 3 \times 5 - 2$

Q4 Calculate $(20 - 6) \times 2 \div 4$

ANSWERS

A1 $20 - 6 \times 2 \div 4 = 20 - 3 = 17$

A2 $\dfrac{15-(4+3)^2}{3-5} = \dfrac{15-49}{-2} = \dfrac{-34}{-2} = 17$

A3 $24 - 3 \times 5 - 2 = 24 - 15 - 2 = 7$

A4 $(20 - 6) \times 2 \div 4 = 14 \times 2 \div 4 = 7$

examiner's note When working with a calculator, either use extra brackets to ensure that calculations are done in the correct order or enter the calculations in chunks as shown in the above solutions.

Standard form

Q1 Without using a calculator, find the value of each of the following, giving your answer in standard form.

(a) $3 \times 10^{12} \times 4 \times 10^{-23}$

(b) $(5 \times 10^8)^2$

(c) $8 \times 10^{13} + 3 \times 10^{12}$

Q2 Using a calculator, find the value of each of the following. Give your answer in standard form, correct to three significant figures where appropriate.

(a) $7.1 \times 10^{21} \div (3.8 \times 10^{-17})$

(b) $8.2 \times 10^{-17} - 6.2 \times 10^{-16}$

ANSWERS

A1 (a) $3 \times 10^{12} \times 4 \times 10^{-23} = 12 \times 10^{-11} = 1.2 \times 10^{-10}$

(b) $(5 \times 10^{8})^{2} = 25 \times 10^{16} = 2.5 \times 10^{17}$

(c) $8 \times 10^{13} + 3 \times 10^{12} = 8 \times 10^{13} + 0.3 \times 10^{13} = 8.3 \times 10^{13}$

A2 (a) $7.1 \times 10^{21} \div (3.8 \times 10^{-17}) = 1.87 \times 10^{38}$

(b) $8.2 \times 10^{-17} - 6.2 \times 10^{-16} = -5.38 \times 10^{-16}$

examiner's note Remember that when you use a calculator to work with numbers in standard form, a result like $-5.38^{\ -16}$ must be written out as -5.38×10^{-16}.

Conversion factors

Q1 (a) Approximately how many miles are there in 200 km?
(b) Approximately how many litres are there in 90 gallons?

Q2 (a) How many km is 65 million cm?
(b) How many ounces are there in 3 stones?

Q3 How many litres are there in a cuboid which is 30 cm by 20 cm by 10 cm?

ANSWERS

A1 (a) 8 km is about 5 miles, so 200 km is approximately $25 \times 5 = 125$ miles

(b) 1 gallon is about 4.5 litres, so 90 gallons is approximately $90 \times 4.5 = 405$ litres (about 400 litres)

A2 (a) 100 cm = 1 m, 100 000 cm = 1 km, and so 1 million cm = 10 km. Therefore 65 million cm = 650 km

(b) 3 st = 3×14 lb = 42 lb = 42×16 oz = 672 ounces

A3 Volume = 30 cm × 20 cm × 10 cm = 6000 cm^3 = 6 litres

examiner's note Writing down the relationships you are using will help you to apply the ratios the correct way round; for example, when converting gallons to litres you have to multiply, not divide, by 4.5 because there must be more litres than gallons in the same volume.

Fractions I: no calculator

Q1 Calculate:

(a) $\frac{1}{4}+\frac{2}{5}$

(b) $\frac{5}{6}-\frac{3}{4}$

Q2 Calculate:

(a) $\frac{7}{8}\times\frac{4}{5}$

(b) $\frac{2}{3}\div\frac{3}{4}$

Q3 Calculate:

(a) $3\frac{1}{4}+2\frac{1}{3}$

(b) $5\frac{2}{3}-2\frac{1}{4}$

Q4 Calculate:

(a) $4\frac{2}{3}+3\frac{1}{2}$

(b) $7\frac{1}{4}-4\frac{1}{2}$

ANSWERS

A1 (a) $\frac{1}{4}+\frac{2}{5}=\frac{5+8}{20}=\frac{13}{20}$

(b) $\frac{5}{6}-\frac{3}{4}=\frac{10-9}{12}=\frac{1}{12}$

A2 (a) $\frac{7}{8}\times\frac{4}{5}=\frac{7\times 4}{8\times 5}=\frac{28}{40}=\frac{7}{10}$

(b) $\frac{2}{3}\div\frac{3}{4}=\frac{2}{3}\times\frac{4}{3}=\frac{8}{9}$

A3 (a) $3\frac{1}{4}+2\frac{1}{3}=5+\frac{3+4}{12}=5\frac{7}{12}$

(b) $5\frac{2}{3}-2\frac{1}{4}=3+\frac{8-3}{12}=3\frac{5}{12}$

A4 (a) $4\frac{2}{3}+3\frac{1}{2}=7+\frac{4+3}{6}=7+1\frac{1}{6}=8\frac{1}{6}$

(b) $7\frac{1}{4}-4\frac{1}{2}=6+1\frac{1}{4}-4\frac{1}{2}=(6-4)+\left(1\frac{1}{4}-\frac{1}{2}\right)=2\frac{3}{4}$

examiner's note Use a common denominator to add or subtract fractions. When multiplying fractions, multiply the top and bottom lines separately.

Fractions II: with calculator

Q1 Calculate:

(a) $\frac{5}{8} \times \frac{7}{22}$

(b) $\frac{6}{19} \div \frac{3}{37}$

Q2 Calculate:

(a) $52\frac{1}{3} + 71\frac{3}{4}$

(b) $46\frac{1}{4} - 38\frac{2}{3}$

Q3 Calculate:

(a) $7\frac{1}{4} \times 5\frac{1}{7}$

(b) $3\frac{1}{4} \div 2\frac{2}{3}$

Q4 Calculate $\left(\frac{5}{8}\right)^2 \div 3\frac{2}{5}$

ANSWERS

A1 (a) $\frac{5}{8} \times \frac{7}{22} = \frac{35}{176}$ (b) $\frac{6}{19} \div \frac{3}{37} = \frac{74}{19} = 3\frac{17}{19}$

A2 (a) $52\frac{1}{3} + 71\frac{3}{4} = 124\frac{1}{12}$ (b) $46\frac{1}{4} - 38\frac{2}{3} = 7\frac{7}{12}$

A3 (a) $7\frac{1}{4} \times 5\frac{1}{7} = 37\frac{2}{7}$ (b) $3\frac{1}{4} \div 2\frac{2}{3} = 1\frac{7}{32}$

A4 $\left(\frac{5}{8}\right)^2 \div 3\frac{2}{5} = \frac{125}{1088}$

examiner's note If your calculator gives $\frac{25}{1088}$ as the answer for Q4, then be sure to use brackets any time you need to square a fraction.

Converting between fractions, decimals and percentages

Give decimals correct to 2 dp and percentages correct to 1 dp where appropriate, and express fractions in their lowest form.

Q1 (a) Change $\frac{4}{5}$ into: (i) a decimal (ii) a percentage

(b) Change $\frac{5}{7}$ into: (i) a decimal (ii) a percentage

Q2 (a) Change 70% into: (i) a decimal (ii) a fraction

(b) Change $17\frac{1}{2}\%$ into: (i) a decimal (ii) a fraction

Q3 (a) Change 0.81 into: (i) a percentage (ii) a fraction

(b) Change $0.\dot{6}$ into: (i) a percentage (ii) a fraction

ANSWERS

A1 (a) (i) 0.8 (ii) 80%

(b) (i) 0.71 (ii) 71.4%

A2 (a) (i) 0.7 (ii) $\frac{70}{100} = \frac{7}{10}$

(b) (i) 0.175 (ii) $\frac{17.5}{100} = \frac{175}{1000} = \frac{7}{40}$

A3 (a) (i) 81% (ii) $\frac{81}{100}$

(b) (i) $0.\dot{6} = 0.666666\ldots = 66.7\%$

(ii) $\frac{2}{3}$

examiner's note You should know the decimal form of common fractions such as the half, thirds, quarters, fifths and eighths.

Working with fractions, decimals and percentages

Q1 Put $\frac{3}{4}$, 0.7, $\frac{7}{6}$, 92% and $\frac{5}{6}$ into ascending order.

Q2 Calculate £3.50 as a fraction of £5. Give your answer in its lowest form.

Q3 Calculate 40 cm as a percentage of 2 metres.

ANSWERS

A1 $\frac{3}{4} = 0.75$, $\frac{7}{6} = 1.1666\ldots$, $92\% = 0.92$, $\frac{5}{6} = 0.8333\ldots$

so in ascending order they are 0.7, $\frac{3}{4}$, $\frac{5}{6}$, 92%, $\frac{7}{6}$

A2 $\frac{£3.50}{£5} = \frac{350}{500} = \frac{7}{10}$

A3 $\frac{40\text{ cm}}{2\text{ m}} = \frac{40\text{ cm}}{200\text{ cm}} = \frac{20}{100} = 20\%$

examiner's note When expressing the relationship between two quantities as a ratio, fraction or percentage, first make sure you are using the same units for the two quantities.

Percentage changes I

Q1 Increase £12 by 6%.

Q2 A shirt is reduced from £15 to £10. Calculate the percentage decrease.

Q3 Keith has an interest-only mortgage of £120 000 at 7% p.a.

(a) Show that his monthly payments are £700.

(b) If the mortgage rate increases to 7.5%, calculate the percentage increase in his monthly payment.

ANSWERS

A1 1% of £12 is 12p, so 6% is 72p. Therefore £12 increased by 6% is £12.72

Alternatively, 1.06 is the multiplying factor for a 6% increase, so the answer is $£12 \times 1.06 = £12.72$

A2 The amount of decrease is £5, so the percentage decrease is

$$\frac{5}{15} \times 100\% = 33.3\%$$

A3 (a) $£120\,000 \times \frac{7}{100} \div 12 = £700$

(b) At 7.5% his monthly payment would be £750, an increase of £50. As a percentage this is

$$\frac{50}{700} \times 100\% = 7.14\%$$

examiner's note Percentage changes are always expressed as a percentage of the **original** value.

Percentage changes II: reverse percentage changes

Q1 A coat is marked at £56 in a sale advertising a 20% discount. What is the full price of the coat?

Q2 A plumber's bill for a job came to £96.35 including VAT. If VAT is charged at $17\frac{1}{2}$%, find the cost of the work done.

Q3 A second-hand car is put on sale for £5000, which would make the dealer a profit of 25% on what he paid for it.

(a) How much did the dealer pay for the car?

(b) After 2 months the dealer decides to reduce the price of the car to what he originally paid for it. What percentage reduction would this be?

ANSWERS

A1 80% is £56, so 1% is 70p and hence 100% is £70
Alternatively, the multiplying factor for a 20% decrease is 0.8, so the original value is £56 ÷ 0.8 = £70

A2 117.5% is £96.35, so 1% is £96.35 ÷ 117.5 = £0.82; hence 100% is £82

Alternatively, the multiplying factor for 17.5% VAT is 1.175, so the value of the work done is £96.35 ÷ 1.175 = £82

A3 (a) 125% is £5000, so 1% is £40 and 100% is £4000

(b) The reduction in price is £1000. As a percentage this is

$$\frac{1000}{5000} \times 100\% = 20\%$$

examiner's note As you can see from Q3, the percentage reduction needed to reverse a percentage increase is not the same as the original percentage change, because the base is different.

Percentage changes III: interest and depreciation

Q1 A car finance company offers a loan of £4000 for 3 years at 5% p.a. simple interest.

(a) Calculate the total amount repayable.

(b) If the loan is to be repaid in 36 equal instalments, explain why the true rate of interest is higher than 5%.

Q2 A woman buys a fixed-interest bond at £12 000. It pays 6% p.a. interest once a year over 5 years. Calculate the value of the bond after 5 years.

A1 (a) Interest $= £4000 \times \frac{5}{100} \times 3 = £600$, so the total amount repayable is £4600.

(b) As time passes, the amount still owing to the finance company gets less and less, but the company will continue to charge interest on the whole of the £4000 borrowed initially, so the actual rate charged on the amount still owed is higher than 5%.

A2 Each year, 6% interest is paid. Doing five separate interest calculations is tedious and time-consuming, so using the multiplying factor is much more sensible. The multiplying factor for a 6% increase is 1.06, so the value after 5 years is $£12\,000 \times 1.06^5 = £16\,058.71$

examiner's note Make sure you write down the expression that you entered into your calculator; otherwise you may miss out on method marks in case your answer is not exactly correct.

Use of a calculator

Q1 Calculate each of the following. Give your answer as an exact value if possible, or in decimal form to 3 sf.

(a) $3\frac{2}{5} - 2\frac{1}{4}$

(b) $\frac{-5 - \sqrt{36 + 32}}{4}$

(c) $\frac{\sqrt{6.2^2 + 7.3}}{5.1 - 3.2}$

(d) $\frac{3.5^2 - \sqrt[3]{12.4}}{6.2 \times 5.1}$

Q2 Find the value of each of the following, giving your answers to 3 sf.

(a) $5.2^2 + 3.1^2 - 2 \times 5.2 \times 3.1 \cos 42°$

(b) $\frac{7 \sin 63°}{\sin 42°}$

(c) $\sin^{-1}\left(\frac{6 \sin 38°}{5.2}\right)$

ANSWERS

A1 (a) $1\frac{3}{20}$

(b) -3.31

(c) 3.56

(d) 0.314

A2 (a) 12.7

(b) 9.32

(c) 45.3°

examiner's note If any calculation is to be done in the denominator, always use brackets to ensure that the order of operations will be correct.

Rounding and estimation

Q1 (a) Round 62.3847 to:

(i) one decimal place (1 dp)

(ii) four significant figures (4 sf)

(b) Round 874 999 to: (i) 5 sf (ii) 3 sf

(c) Round 0.003 175 to: (i) 3 dp (ii) 3 sf

Q2 Estimate the values of:

(a) $\dfrac{61.7 + 89.1}{3.1 \times 5.1}$

(b) $\dfrac{403.2 + 796.1}{7.3^2}$

ANSWERS

A1 (a) (i) 62.4 (1 dp) (ii) 62.38 (4 sf)

(b) (i) 875 000 (5 sf) (ii) 875 000 (3 sf)

Although these two answers look the same, in (i) the left two zeros are significant, i.e. they each represent an actual 0 rather than 1, 2, 3 or 4; in (ii), however, all three zeros are there purely for place value.

(c) (i) 0.003 (3 dp) (ii) 0.00318 (3 sf)

A2 (a) $\frac{61.7+89.1}{3.1\times 5.1} \approx \frac{60+90}{3\times 5} = \frac{150}{15} = 10$

(b) $\frac{403.2+796.1}{7.3^2} \approx \frac{400+800}{50} = \frac{1200}{50} = 24$

examiner's note Always state the accuracy of any rounding that you have done — in this way a distinction can be made between, for example, the numbers in Q1(b) parts (i) and (ii).

Ratio and proportional division

Q1 Express the following as ratios in their lowest form:

(a) 45 : 36

(b) £9 : 72p

Q2 (a) Divide £100 000 in the ratio 3 : 2.

(b) £240 000 is to be divided between Louise, Joanne and Laura in the ratio 3 : 2 : 1. How much does Louise get?

ANSWERS

A1 (a) 5 : 4

(b) £9 : 72p = 900p : 72p = 900 : 72 = 100 : 8 = 25 : 2

Note that in part (b), the quantities must be expressed in the same units before anything else can be done; but once both quantities have been put in the same units, those units should be removed, as a ratio is purely numerical.

A2 (a) To divide £100 000 in the ratio 3 : 2, we make a total of $3 + 2 = 5$ equal parts, so each part is worth £20 000. The division of money is therefore £60 000 : £40 000.

(b) With a ratio of three, the principle is the same as in (a). A 3 : 2 : 1 ratio means dividing £240 000 into $3 + 2 + 1 = 6$ equal parts, so each part is worth £40 000. Louise's share is £40 000 × 3 = £120 000.

***examiner's* note** Remember to include units in answers where appropriate.

Powers, roots and indices I

Q1 (a) Write $2 \times 2 \times 2 \times 2 \times 2 \times 2$ as a power of 2.

(b) Write $\dfrac{1}{3 \times 3 \times 3 \times 3}$ as a power of 3.

Q2 Without using a calculator, work out the value of:

(a) $\sqrt{49}$

(b) 2^3

(c) $\sqrt[3]{125}$

Q3 Calculate $\left(\dfrac{5}{3}\right)^3$

ANSWERS

A1 (a) $2 \times 2 \times 2 \times 2 \times 2 \times 2 = 2^6$

(b) $\dfrac{1}{3 \times 3 \times 3 \times 3} = 3^{-4}$

A2 (a) 7

(b) 8

(c) 5

A3 $\dfrac{125}{27}$

examiner's note Be aware that when taking the power of a fraction, many calculators will apply the power only to the last digit entered. Check whether this is the case with your calculator by taking the square of 2/3; if you get 2/9 as the answer, then you need to put brackets around fractions.

Powers, roots and indices II

Q1 Write each of the following as a simple power (in the form a^b):

(a) $5^{12} \times 5^4$ (b) $7^{24} \div 7^8$ (c) $(4^2)^3$ (d) $\dfrac{6^{12} \times 6^{-8}}{6^{-3}}$ (e) $\dfrac{1}{4}$

Q2 For each of the following, calculate the value if possible, giving your answer as a decimal correct to two decimal places where appropriate:

(a) $7^{\frac{1}{2}}$ (b) $(-64)^{\frac{1}{3}}$ (c) $(-8)^{\frac{1}{2}}$

Q3 Calculate $\left(\dfrac{9}{4}\right)^{\frac{3}{2}}$

ANSWERS

A1 (a) $5^{12} \times 5^4 = 5^{12+4} = 5^{16}$

(b) $7^{24} \div 7^8 = 7^{24-8} = 7^{16}$

(c) $(4^2)^3 = 4^{2\times3} = 4^6$

(d) $\dfrac{6^{12} \times 6^{-8}}{6^{-3}} = 6^{12-8-(-3)} = 6^7$

(e) 4^{-1} or 2^{-2}

A2 (a) $7^{\frac{1}{2}} = \sqrt{7} = 2.65$ (to 2 dp)

(b) $(-64)^{\frac{1}{3}} = \sqrt[3]{-64} = -4$

(c) $(-8)^{\frac{1}{2}} = \sqrt{-8}$ does not exist

A3 $\left(\dfrac{9}{4}\right)^{\frac{3}{2}} = \sqrt{\left(\dfrac{9}{4}\right)^3} = \sqrt{\dfrac{729}{64}} = \dfrac{27}{8}$ or $\left(\dfrac{9}{4}\right)^{\frac{3}{2}} = \left(\sqrt{\dfrac{9}{4}}\right)^3 = \left(\dfrac{3}{2}\right)^3 = \dfrac{27}{8}$

examiner's note Calculating a fractional (a/b) power means to take the bth root and raise to the ath power — in either order, whichever is easier.

Powers, roots and indices III

Answer the following questions without using a calculator.

Q1 Calculate the value of:

(a) 2^3

(b) $3^2 - 2^3$

Q2 Write each of the following as a fraction or a whole number:

(a) 5^{-2}

(b) $\left(\frac{2}{3}\right)^2$

(c) $\left(\frac{2}{3}\right)^{-2}$

(d) $\left(\frac{2}{3}\right)^0$

ANSWERS

A1 (a) $2^3 = 2 \times 2 \times 2 = 8$

(b) $3^2 - 2^3 = 9 - 8 = 1$

A2 (a) $5^{-2} = \frac{1}{5^2} = \frac{1}{25}$

(b) $\left(\frac{2}{3}\right)^2 = \frac{2^2}{3^2} = \frac{4}{9}$

(c) $\left(\frac{2}{3}\right)^{-2} = \frac{1}{\left(\frac{2}{3}\right)^2} = \left(\frac{3}{2}\right)^2 = \frac{9}{4}$

(d) 1

***examiner's* note** Remember that $x^0 = 1$ for any value of x.

Upper and lower bounds

Q1 Given that $a = 13.2$ and $b = 7.1$, each correct to 1 dp, find upper and lower bounds for:

(i) $a + b$

(ii) $a - b$

(iii) $a \times b$

(iv) $a \div b$

Q2 A car using cruise control travels at 65 mph (correct to the nearest mph) for a period of 20 minutes (correct to the nearest minute). What is the least distance that the car could have travelled?

ANSWERS

A1 Since both values are correct to 1 dp, a is between 13.15 and 13.25, and b is between 7.05 and 7.15.

(i) Lower bound $13.15 + 7.05 = 20.2$
Upper bound $13.25 + 7.15 = 20.4$

(ii) Lower bound $13.15 - 7.15 = 6.0$
Upper bound $13.25 - 7.05 = 6.2$

(iii) Lower bound $13.15 \times 7.05 = 92.7075$
Upper bound $13.25 \times 7.15 = 94.7375$

(iv) Lower bound $13.15 \div 7.15 = 1.839\ldots$
Upper bound $13.25 \div 7.05 = 1.879\ldots$

A2 The minimum distance travelled would result from combining the lowest possible speed with the shortest possible time, i.e. 64.5 mph and 19.5 minutes.

$$\text{Least distance} = 64.5\frac{\text{miles}}{\text{hr}} \times \frac{19.5}{60}\text{hr} = 20.9625 \text{ miles}$$

examiner's note If in doubt as to which combination of smallest and largest values will give the upper or lower bound, you can always try all four possible combinations.

Direct and inverse proportion

Q1 Given that $y = 7x^2$, find:

(a) y when $x = 2$

(b) x when $y = 63$

Q2 y is directly proportional to x and $y = 36$ when $x = 9$.

(a) Find an expression for y in terms of x.

(b) (i) Find the value of y when $x = 2$.

(ii) Find the value of x when $y = 12$.

Q3 y is inversely proportional to x and $y = 6$ when $x = 7$.

(a) Find an expression for y in terms of x.

(b) (i) Find the value of y when $x = 3$.

(ii) Find the value of x when $y = 5$.

ANSWERS

A1 (a) When $x = 2$, $y = 7 \times 2^2 = 7 \times 4 = 28$

(b) When $y = 63$, we have $63 = 7x^2$, hence $x^2 = 9$ and so $x = \pm 3$

A2 (a) y directly proportional to x means $y = kx$

$y = 36$ when $x = 9 \Rightarrow 36 = 9k \Rightarrow k = 4$, so $y = 4x$

(b) (i) When $x = 2$, $y = 4 \times 2 = 8$

(ii) When $y = 12$, we have $12 = 4x$, so $x = 3$

A3 (a) y inversely proportional to x means $y = \dfrac{k}{x}$

$y = 6$ when $x = 7 \Rightarrow 6 = \dfrac{k}{7} \Rightarrow k = 42$, so $y = \dfrac{42}{x}$

(b) (i) When $x = 3$, $y = \dfrac{42}{3} = 14$

(ii) When $y = 5$, we have $5 = \dfrac{42}{x}$, so $x = \dfrac{42}{5} = 8.4$

examiner's note From the description of the proportionality relationship, first write down the equation with k in it; then everything else is just substitution.

Rational and irrational numbers

Q1 State whether or not each of the following numbers is rational:

(a) π^2 (b) $\frac{7}{3}$ (c) 1.63

(d) $\sqrt{\frac{4}{25}}$ (e) $\sqrt{\frac{9}{47}}$

Q2 Give an irrational number between 2.1 and 2.2.

Q3 Express $0.\dot{1}5\dot{6}$ as a fraction in its lowest form.

ANSWERS

A1 (a) π^2 is irrational

(b) $\frac{7}{3}$ is a fraction and therefore rational

(c) $1.63 = \frac{163}{100}$, a fraction and so rational

(d) $\sqrt{\frac{4}{25}} = \frac{2}{5}$ is rational (e) $\sqrt{\frac{9}{47}} = \frac{3}{\sqrt{47}}$ is irrational

A2 $2.1^2 = 4.41$ and $2.2^2 = 4.84$, so $\sqrt{4.5}$ is an irrational number that lies between 2.1 and 2.2.
Alternatively, $\pi = 3.14159...$, so $\pi - 1 = 2.14159...$ is an irrational number that lies between 2.1 and 2.2.

A3 $x = 0.156156156...$ $1000x = 156.156156...$
Subtracting the first line from the second gives

$999x = 156$ so $x = \frac{156}{999} = \frac{52}{333}$

***examiner's* note** All fractions and recurring or terminating decimals are rational numbers.

Surds

Q1 Write the following as surds in their simplest form:

(a) $\sqrt{20}$

(b) $\sqrt{24}$

(c) $\sqrt{2} + \sqrt{18}$

Q2 Simplify:

(a) $\dfrac{14}{\sqrt{6}}$

(b) $\dfrac{15}{\sqrt{5}}$

Q3 Expand and simplify:

(a) $(3 + \sqrt{5})(2 - \sqrt{5})$

(b) $(\sqrt{3} + 2\sqrt{5})(4\sqrt{3} - \sqrt{5})$

ANSWERS

A1 (a) $\sqrt{20} = \sqrt{4 \times 5} = 2\sqrt{5}$

(b) $\sqrt{24} = \sqrt{4 \times 6} = 2\sqrt{6}$

(c) $\sqrt{2} + \sqrt{18} = \sqrt{2} + \sqrt{9 \times 2} = \sqrt{2} + 3\sqrt{2} = 4\sqrt{2}$

A2 (a) $\dfrac{14}{\sqrt{6}} = \dfrac{14}{\sqrt{6}} \times \dfrac{\sqrt{6}}{\sqrt{6}} = \dfrac{14\sqrt{6}}{6} = \dfrac{7\sqrt{6}}{3}$

(b) $\dfrac{15}{\sqrt{5}} = \dfrac{15}{\sqrt{5}} \times \dfrac{\sqrt{5}}{\sqrt{5}} = \dfrac{15\sqrt{5}}{5} = 3\sqrt{5}$

A3 (a) $(3 + \sqrt{5})(2 - \sqrt{5}) = 6 - 3\sqrt{5} + 2\sqrt{5} - 5 = 1 - \sqrt{5}$

(b) $(\sqrt{3} + 2\sqrt{5})(4\sqrt{3} - \sqrt{5}) = 12 - \sqrt{15} + 8\sqrt{15} - 10 = 2 + 7\sqrt{15}$

examiner's note Upon multiplying similar surds together, immediately write the result as an integer — for example, write $\sqrt{5} \times \sqrt{5}$ directly as 5, not $\sqrt{25}$.

Exponential growth and decay

Q1 A colony of bacteria doubles in size every day. On Tuesday morning there are 500 cells.

(a) How many cells will there be on Friday morning?

(b) How many cells will there be on Tuesday morning of the next week?

(c) How long will it be before there are a million cells?

Q2 (a) Sketch the graph of $y = 2^x$.

(b) On the same axes sketch the graph of $y = 3^{-x}$.

ANSWERS

A1 (a) $500 \times 2^3 = 4000$

(b) $500 \times 2^7 = 64\,000$

(c) $500 \times 2^{10} = 512\,000$ and $500 \times 2^{11} = 1\,024\,000$, so it will be the Saturday of the next week that the bacteria population reaches 1 million cells.

A2

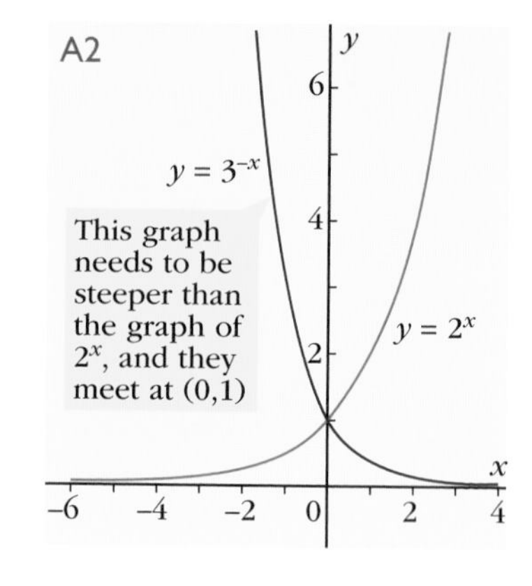

examiner's note Calculating the coordinates of a small number of points on an exponential graph will give you a good idea of how steeply the curve rises or falls.

Written communication in number

Q1 The prices of entrance at a zoo are £8 for an adult and £5 for a child (under 16 years). The zoo offers a family ticket for up to four people (maximum two adults) that costs £20.

James wants to take his children Catharine (12 years old) and Wayne to the zoo on Saturday to celebrate Wayne's 16th birthday, which is on Thursday. He wants to pay as little as possible while paying what he should.

Should James buy a family ticket? Show your reasoning fully.

ANSWERS

A1 On Saturday Wayne will be 16 and will count as an adult. James can pay £20 for a family ticket or 2 × £8 + £5 = £21 for individual entrances, so a family ticket would be cheaper.

Note that if they were to go before Wayne's birthday, the cost of individual entrances for the three of them, £8 + 2 × £5 = £18, would be lower than the price of the family ticket.

examiner's note When asked to show your reasoning, be particularly careful to explain the development of your answer clearly. This is the sort of question that could be used to assess written communication in number.

Simplifying expressions

Q1 Simplify $5x + 2y + 3x - 5y$

Q2 Simplify $4x^2y + 3xy - 2xy^2 + 7xy$

Q3 Expand and simplify $5(2x + 3y) - 2(4x - 5y)$

Q4 Factorise $7xy + 14y$

Q5 Factorise $10y + 5$

ANSWERS

A1 $8x - 3y$

A2 $4x^2y + 10xy - 2xy^2$

A3 $5(2x + 3y) - 2(4x - 5y) = 10x + 15y - 8x + 10y = 2x + 25y$

A4 $7y(x + 2)$

A5 $5(2y + 1)$

examiner's note Before you try to combine terms, make sure their algebraic parts are exactly the same; for example, in Q2 the x^2y and xy^2 are different and so these terms cannot be combined.

Coordinates and linear graphs

Q1 Draw the lines $x = -2$ and $y = 4$.

Q2 (a) Draw the line $y = 3x - 2$.

(b) State the gradient and y-intercept of $y = 3x - 2$.

Q3 For $3y = 7x - 5$ find the gradient and y-intercept.

Q4 Which of the following are straight lines?

A: $y = 2x - 7$ B: $y = x^2 + 3$

C: $y(x + 3) = 2$ D: $5x + 2y + 7 = 0$

ANSWERS

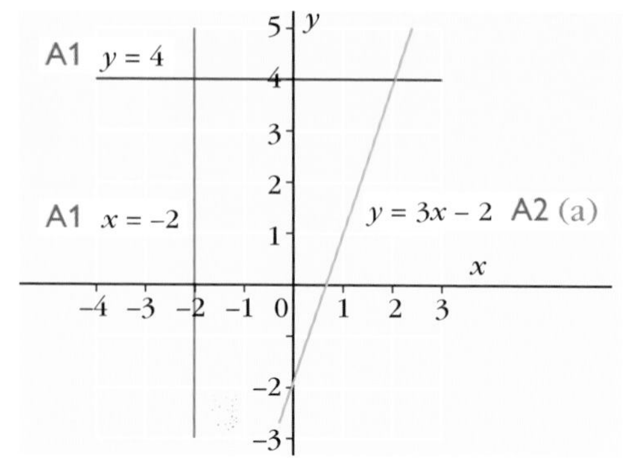

A2 (b) Gradient is 3; y-intercept is $(0, -2)$

A3 $y = \frac{7}{3}x - \frac{5}{3}$, so the gradient is $\frac{7}{3}$ and the y-intercept is $(0, -\frac{5}{3})$

A4 A and D are straight lines.

examiner's note The simplest way to identify the gradient and y-intercept of a straight line is to rearrange the equation into the form $y = \dots$.

Inequalities and graphs

Q1 Solve $3x - 1 \geq 11$

Q2 Solve $5x + 3 < 2x - 4$ and show the solution on a number line.

Q3 Solve $2x + 3 \leq 3x - 2$

Q4 On a graph, show the region for which $\begin{cases} x + 3y \geq 6 \\ y < \frac{1}{2}x \\ x < 5 \end{cases}$

ANSWERS

A1 $3x - 1 \geq 11$

$\Rightarrow 3x \geq 12$

$\Rightarrow x \geq 4$

A2 $5x + 3 < 2x - 4$

$\Rightarrow 3x < -7$

$\Rightarrow x < -\dfrac{7}{3}$

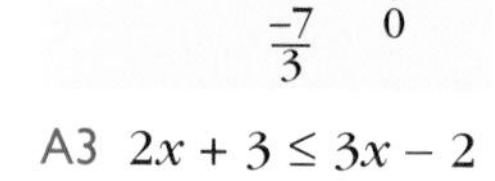

A3 $2x + 3 \leq 3x - 2$

$\Rightarrow -x \leq -5$

$\Rightarrow x \geq 5$

or:

$2x + 3 \leq 3x - 2$

$\Rightarrow 5 \leq x$

$\Rightarrow x \geq 5$

A4

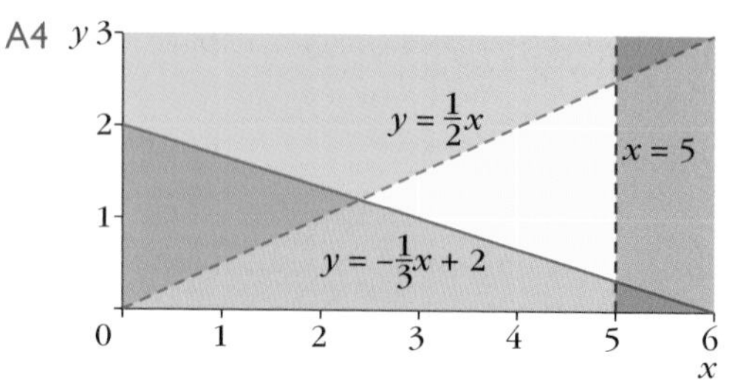

The unshaded region is where $x + 3y \geq 6$, $y < \frac{1}{2}x$ and $x < 5$. Note that the vertical line and the upward-sloping line should be drawn as broken (dashed) lines.

examiner's note If you multiply or divide through an inequality by a negative number, remember that the direction of the inequality has to be reversed.

Linear sequences

Q1 The nth term of a sequence is given by $5n - 2$. Write down the first three terms and the 40th term in the sequence.

Q2 The nth term of a sequence is given by $25 - 2n$. Write down the first three terms and the 35th term in the sequence.

Q3 For each of the following sequences, find an expression for the nth term:

(a) 7, 10, 13, 16, 19,…

(b) 2, 7, 12, 17, 22,…

(c) 23, 18, 13, 8, 3,…

ANSWERS

A1 The first three terms are 3, 8, 13
and the 40th term is $5 \times 40 - 2 = 198$.

A2 The first three terms are 23, 21, 19
and the 35th term is $25 - 2 \times 35 = -45$.

A3 (a) The common difference is 3 and $7 - 3 = 4$
so the nth term is $3n + 4$

(b) The common difference is 5 and $2 - 5 = -3$
so the nth term is $5n - 3$

(c) The common difference is -5 and $23 - (-5) = 28$
so the nth term is $-5n + 28$

examiner's note If the sequence is decreasing, the expression for the nth term will have a negative coefficient for n.

Trial and improvement

Q1 (a) Show that $x^3 + 3x^2 = 3$ has a solution between 0 and 1.

(b) Find the solution correct to two decimal places.

Q2 (a) Show that $x^3 - 2x = 20$ has a solution between 2 and 3.

(b) Find the solution correct to one decimal place.

ANSWERS

A1 (a) The value of $x^3 + 3x^2$ is 0 (< 3) when $x = 0$ and 4 (> 3) when $x = 1$, so there is a solution to $x^3 + 3x^2 = 3$ for x between 0 and 1.

(b)

x	$x^3 + 3x^2$
0.8	2.432
0.9	3.159
0.88	3.004 672
0.87	2.929 203
0.875	2.966...

So the solution lies between 0.875 and 0.88. It is 0.88 correct to 2 dp.

A2 (a) The value of $x^3 - 2x$ is 4 (< 20) when $x = 2$ and 21 (> 20) when $x = 3$, so there is a solution to $x^3 - 2x = 20$ for x between 2 and 3.

(b)

x	$x^3 - 2x$
2.8	16.352
2.9	18.589
3.0	21
2.95	19.772...

So the solution lies between 2.95 and 3.0. It is 3.0 correct to 1 dp.

examiner's note The answer in 2(b) needs to be given as 3.0 to show that the value is correct to one decimal place.

Solving linear equations

Q1 Solve $3x + 1 = 7$

Q2 Solve $3x - 2 = 5x + 3$

Q3 Solve $2(x - 3) + 3(x - 1) = 4x - 2$

Q4 Solve $\frac{5x}{3} - 7 = x + 4$

ANSWERS

A1 $3x + 1 = 7$

$(-1) \Rightarrow 3x = 6$

$(\div 3) \Rightarrow x = 2$

A2 $3x - 2 = 5x + 3$

$(-3x) \Rightarrow -2 = 2x + 3$

$(-3) \Rightarrow -5 = 2x$

$(\div 2) \Rightarrow x = -2.5$

A3 $2(x - 3) + 3(x - 1) = 4x - 2$

$\Rightarrow 2x - 6 + 3x - 3 = 4x - 2$

$\Rightarrow 5x - 9 = 4x - 2$

$(-4x) \Rightarrow x - 9 = -2$

$(+9) \Rightarrow x = 7$

A4 $\frac{5x}{3} - 7 = x + 4$

$(\times 3) \Rightarrow 5x - 21 = 3x + 12$

$(-3x) \Rightarrow 2x - 21 = 12$

$(+21) \Rightarrow 2x = 33$

$(\div 2) \Rightarrow x = 16.5$

***examiner's* note** Answers can be fractions or negative numbers, so don't be surprised if the result you get doesn't look 'nice'.

Rearranging formulae I

In each of the following, make the letter enclosed in [ ] the subject of the formula.

Q1 $\frac{x}{a} + b = y$ [x]

Q2 $a(x - b) = P$ [x]

Q3 $a(x - 3) + b(x + 2) = y$ [x]

Q4 $V = \frac{1}{3}\pi r^2 h$ [h]

ANSWERS

A1 $\frac{x}{a} + b = y \Rightarrow x + ab = ay \Rightarrow x = ay - ab$

A2 $a(x - b) = P \Rightarrow ax - ab = P \Rightarrow ax = P + ab \Rightarrow x = \frac{P}{a} + b$

or: $a(x - b) = P \Rightarrow x - b = \frac{P}{a} \Rightarrow x = \frac{P}{a} + b$

A3 $a(x - 3) + b(x + 2) = y \Rightarrow ax - 3a + bx + 2b = y$

$$\Rightarrow ax + bx = y + 3a - 2b$$

$$\Rightarrow x(a + b) = y + 3a - 2b$$

$$\Rightarrow x = \frac{y + 3a - 2b}{a + b}$$

A4 $V = \frac{1}{3}\pi r^2 h \Rightarrow h = \frac{V}{\frac{1}{3}\pi r^2} = \frac{3V}{\pi r^2}$

examiner's note Do only one operation at a time, and always do the same to both sides of the equation.

Rearranging formulae II

In each of the following, make the letter enclosed in [ ] the subject of the formula.

Q1 $y = \dfrac{4 - 2x}{2x - 1}$ [x]

Q2 $r + 2\sqrt{h} = 5r + 6$ [h]

Q3 $V = \dfrac{1}{3}\pi r^2 h$ [r]

ANSWERS

A1 $y = \dfrac{4-2x}{2x-1} \Rightarrow 2xy - y = 4 - 2x$

$$\Rightarrow 2xy + 2x = 4 + y$$

$$\Rightarrow 2x(y + 1) = 4 + y$$

$$\Rightarrow x = \frac{4+y}{2(y+1)}$$

A2 $r + 2\sqrt{h} = 5r + 6 \Rightarrow 2\sqrt{h} = 4r + 6 \Rightarrow \sqrt{h} = 2r + 3$

$$\Rightarrow h = (2r + 3)^2$$

A3 $V = \dfrac{1}{3}\pi r^2 h \Rightarrow r^2 = \dfrac{V}{\frac{1}{3}\pi h} = \dfrac{3V}{\pi h} \Rightarrow r = \sqrt{\dfrac{3V}{\pi h}}$

examiner's note If the new subject appears twice (or more times) in the equation, first collect together all terms that contain it and then take it out as a common factor.

Gradients and finding the equation of a line

Q1 A is (–1, 1) and B is (2, 7).

(a) Find the gradient of AB.

(b) Find the equation of the line AB.

Q2 Find the equation of the line that passes through (–2, 1) and (4, –1).

Q3 The graph of $y = x^2 - 2x + 3$ is shown. Find the equation of the tangent to the curve at (2, 3).

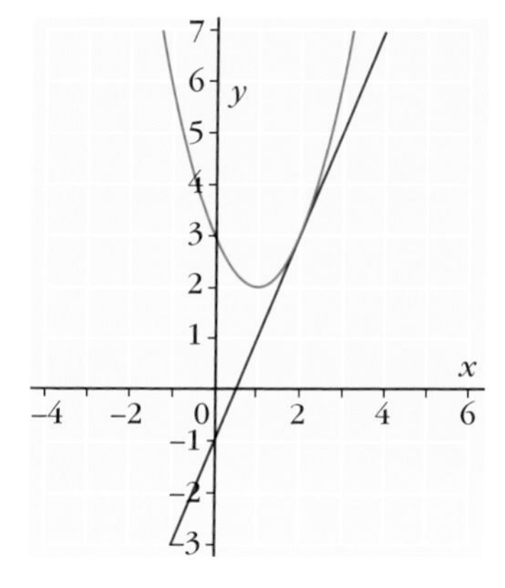

ANSWERS

A1 (a) Gradient $= \dfrac{7-1}{2-(-1)} = \dfrac{6}{3} = 2$

(b) The line AB is $y = 2x + c$ and goes through (2, 7).
Substituting $y = 7$ and $x = 2$ gives $7 = 2 \times 2 + c$, so $c = 3$.
Therefore the equation of AB is $y = 2x + 3$

A2 Gradient $= \dfrac{-1-1}{4-(-2)} = \dfrac{-2}{6} = -\dfrac{1}{3}$

The line has equation $y = -\dfrac{1}{3}x + \dfrac{1}{3}$

A3 (0, –1) and (2, 3) lie on the tangent, so gradient of tangent is $\dfrac{3-(-1)}{2-0} = \dfrac{4}{2} = 2$. Equation is $y = 2x - 1$

examiner's note Be careful with negative coordinates when calculating the rise and run to find a gradient — use the graph to check the distances you obtain.

Parallel and perpendicular lines

Q1 From the list below, find:

(a) two pairs of parallel lines

(b) two pairs of perpendicular lines

A: $y = 3x - 7$	B: $y = 2x - 7$	C: $y = -3x + 2$
D: $y = 4$	E: $y + 3x = 6$	F: $x = 4$
G: $y = \frac{1}{3}x + 7$	H: $y = -2$	

Q2 (a) Write down the equation of a line parallel to $y = -2x + 1$.

(b) Find the equation of the line perpendicular to $y = -2x + 1$ which goes through (6, 2).

Q3 Are $y = -2x + 4$ and $3y + 6x - 12 = 0$ parallel?

ANSWERS

A1 (a) E can be rewritten as $y = -3x + 6$, so C and E are parallel. D and H are both vertical lines, so they are parallel, too.

(b) The gradient of G, $\frac{1}{3}$, multiplies with the gradient of C or E (−3) to give −1, so G is perpendicular to both C and E. F is a horizontal line, so it is perpendicular to both D and H.

A2 (a) Any line with equation $y = -2x + c$ where c is not 1

(b) Any line perpendicular to $y = -2x + 1$ must have gradient $\frac{1}{2}$ (since $-2 \times \frac{1}{2} = -1$), so the equation is $y = \frac{1}{2}x + c$. For the line to go through (6, 2) requires that $2 = \frac{1}{2} \times 6 + c$, giving $c = -1$. Therefore the line has equation $y = \frac{1}{2}x - 1$

A3 The second equation can be rearranged to $y = -2x + 4$, so the given equations actually represent the same line (rather than just parallel lines).

***examiner's* note** Gradients of lines that are perpendicular to each other always multiply to give −1 (except for a horizontal–vertical pair of lines).

Conversion graphs

Q1 A travel agent advertises a foreign exchange service with 'no commission'. He will sell euros at a rate of €1.20 to the pound, and buy euros at a rate of €1.32 to the pound.

(a) Anneka changes £250 into euros. How many euros does she get?

(b) Anneka has to change her holiday plans. How much will the travel agent give her back for the euros?

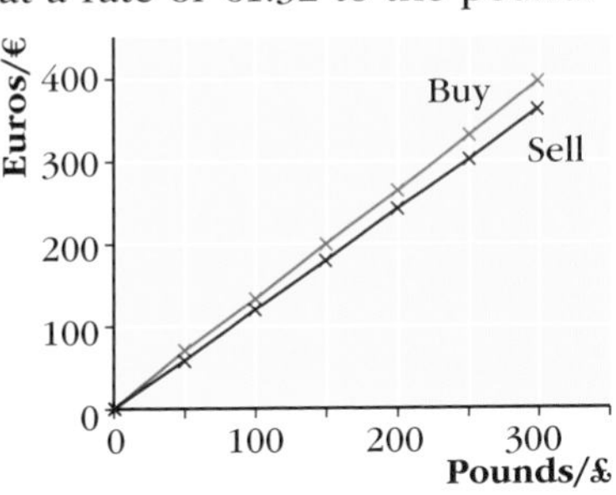

ANSWERS

A1 (a) From the graph, go up from 250 on the horizontal axis to the blue line representing the 'sell' rate of the travel agent, and then go across to the vertical axis and read off the value there; this tells us that Anneka will get €300 for her £250.

(b) Anneka wants the travel agent to buy her €300 back. So find 300 on the vertical scale, but now go across to the red line, which represents the exchange rate at which the travel agent will buy euros. Then, by going vertically down to the horizontal axis, you can estimate that Anneka will get about £225 back for the €300. (With the given exchange rate of €1.32 to £1, you could calculate the value as £227.27 to the nearest penny.)

examiner's note When using conversion graphs, you are only expected to give your answer to a reasonable degree of accuracy, so there is no need to spend a long time trying to determine the exact value.

Interpretation of graphs I

Q1 A car hire firm charges a flat rate to hire a car for a day, provided the user does not exceed a certain number (n) of miles. Any additional miles are charged at x pence per mile. The graph shows the cost of hiring the car for a day for up to 550 miles.

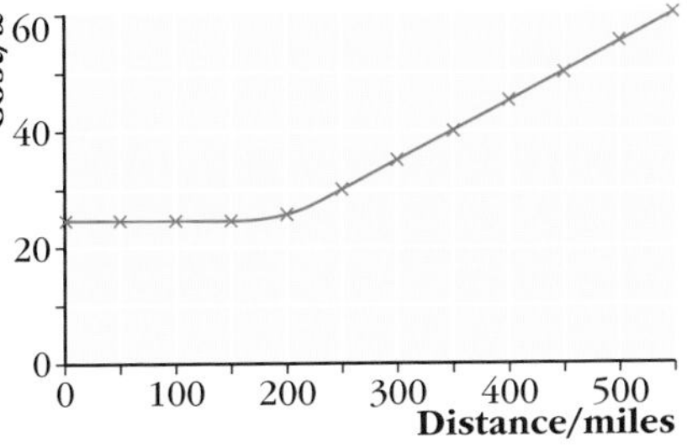

(a) Use the graph to work out the value of n and the flat rate charge.

(b) Use the graph to work out the value of x.

A1 The cost stays at £25 up to 200 miles and then starts to increase, so $n = 200$ and the flat rate charge is £25.

A2 The gradient of the upward-sloping line beyond 200 miles will give the extra cost per mile. At 300 miles the charge is £35, so an extra 100 miles costs an extra £10, giving a rate of 10p per mile beyond the 200 miles included in the basic charge.

***examiner's* note** The gradient is always the increase in y for a **unit increase** in x, and its units will depend on the context, i.e. what quantities are represented on the x and y axes.

Interpretation of graphs II

Q1 A sphere is being filled with water at a constant rate. Sketch a graph of the depth of water in the sphere against time.

Q2 A taxi charges £2.50 for the first 0.7 miles and then 20p for each tenth of a mile (or part thereof) after the first 0.7 miles.

(a) How much will a journey of 1.4 miles cost?

(b) How much will a journey of 1.65 miles cost?

(c) Sketch a graph of cost against journey length for the taxi.

ANSWERS

A1

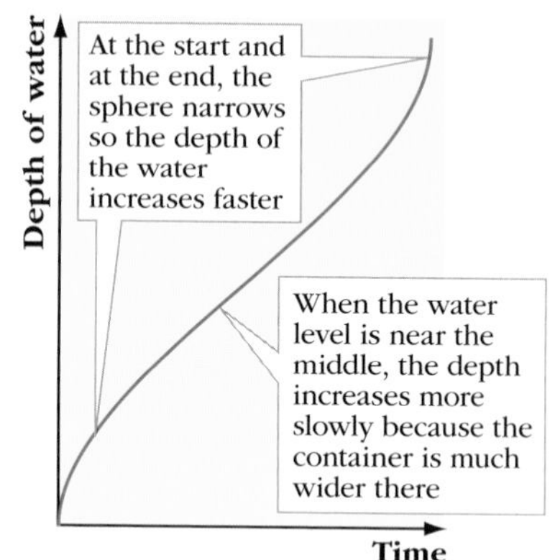

A2 (a) £2.50 + 7 × 20p = £3.90.

(b) £2.50 + 10 × 20p = £4.50.

(c) Up to 0.7 miles the graph is flat at £2.50; it will then be a step graph that jumps up by £0.20 for every 0.1 mile increase in distance.

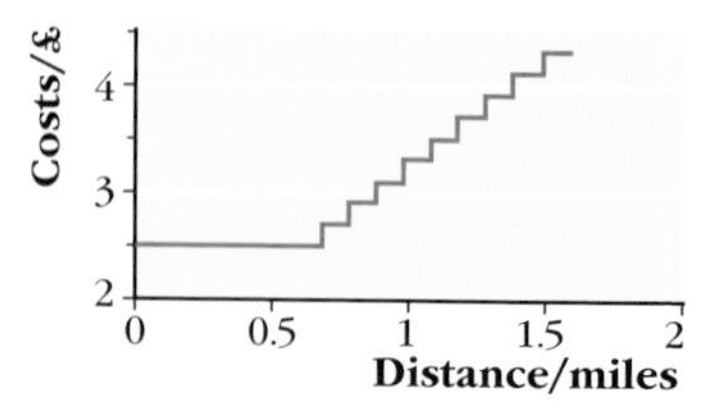

examiner's note When sketching a graph, it is often easier to think in terms of **rate of change** of a quantity (i.e. the slope of the graph) — consider whether it is increasing (graph getting steeper) or decreasing (graph getting flatter).

Quadratic graphs

Q1 (a) Construct a table of values of $y = x^2 - 2x - 4$ for $x = -2$ to 4.

(b) Draw the graph of $y = x^2 - 2x - 4$.

Q2 (a) (i) Show that $x^2 - 6x + 5$ can be written as $(x - 3)^2 - 4$.

(ii) Write down the coordinates of the turning point of $y = x^2 - 6x + 5$.

(b) Sketch the graph of $y = x^2 - 6x + 5$.

ANSWERS

A1 (a)

x	−2	−1	0	1	2	3	4
x^2	4	1	0	1	4	9	16
$-2x$	4	2	0	−2	−4	−6	−8
-4	−4	−4	−4	−4	−4	−4	−4
y	4	−1	−4	−5	−4	−1	4

(b)

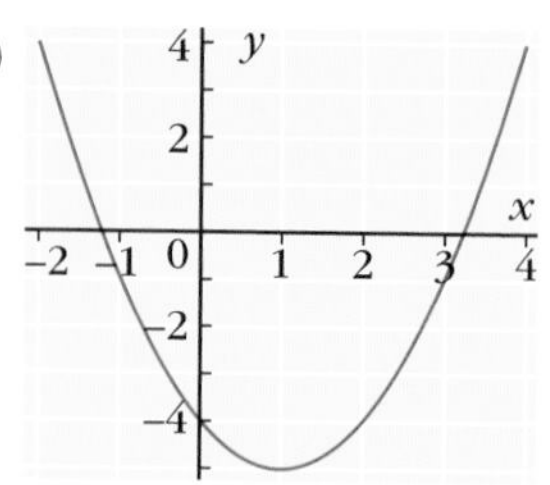

A2 (a) (i) $(x-3)^2 = x^2 - 6x + 9$, so (upon subtracting 4 from both sides) $x^2 - 6x + 5 = (x-3)^2 - 4$

(ii) The turning point occurs when $(x-3)^2 = 0$, i.e. when $x = 3$. At this point we have $y = -4$, so the coordinates of the turning point are $(3, -4)$.

(b)

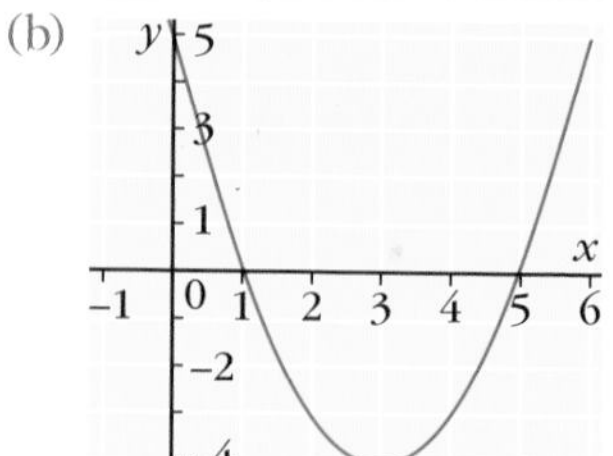

examiner's note The graph of a quadratic is always a smooth curve with a vertical line of symmetry; the curve will often go beyond the highest or lowest point in the table of values that you make.

More graphs: cubic, reciprocal and circles

Q1 Given that $x^3 - 4x^2 + x + 6 = (x + 1)(x - 2)(x - 3)$, sketch the graph of $y = x^3 - 4x^2 + x + 6$.

Q2 Sketch the graph of $x^2 + y^2 = 16$.

Q3 Sketch the graphs of:

(a) $y = \dfrac{-12}{x}$

(b) $y = \dfrac{36}{x^2}$

ANSWERS

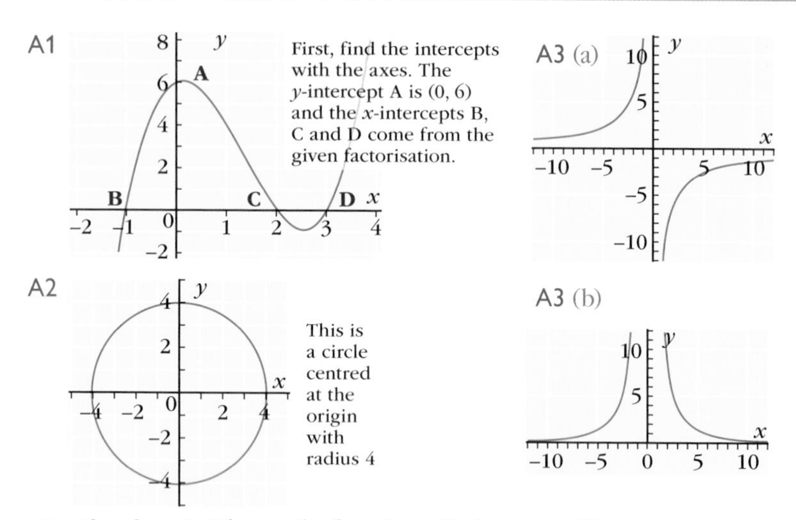

examiner's note The graph of a cubic will always go off in opposite directions at the two ends, and it must cut the x-axis at least once and no more than three times.

Factorising quadratics I

Q1 Factorise $y^2 - 25$

Q2 Factorise $x^2 - 2x - 15$

Q3 Factorise $x^2 - 5x + 6$

Q4 Factorise $20x^2 - 45y^2$

ANSWERS

A1 $y^2 - 25 = (y + 5)(y - 5)$

A2 $x^2 - 2x - 15 = x^2 - 5x + 3x - 5 \times 3 = (x - 5)(x + 3)$

A3 $x^2 - 5x + 6 = x^2 - 3x - 2x + (-3) \times (-2) = (x - 3)(x - 2)$

A4 $20x^2 - 45y^2 = 5(4x^2 - 9y^2) = 5(2x + 3y)(2x - 3y)$

examiner's note When the quadratic term is just x^2 (i.e. the coefficient is 1), look for two numbers whose product is the constant term and whose sum is the coefficient of x.

Factorising quadratics II

Q1 Factorise $2x^2 - 5x - 3$

Q2 Factorise $3x^2 - 7x + 2$

Q3 Factorise $6x^2 + 7x - 3$

Q4 Factorise $12x^2 - 23x + 5$

ANSWERS

A1 $2x^2 - 5x - 3 = 2x^2 \mathbf{- 6}x \mathbf{+ 1}x - 3$ [product −6, sum −5]

$= 2x(x - 3) + 1(x - 3) = (x - 3)(2x + 1)$

A2 $3x^2 - 7x + 2 = 3x^2 \mathbf{- 6}x \mathbf{- 1}x + 2$ [product +6, sum −7]

$= 3x(x - 2) - 1(x - 2) = (x - 2)(3x - 1)$

A3 $6x^2 + 7x - 3 = 6x^2 \mathbf{+ 9}x \mathbf{- 2}x - 3$ [product −18, sum +7]

$= 3x(2x + 3) - 1(2x + 3) = (2x + 3)(3x - 1)$

A4 $12x^2 - 23x + 5 = 12x^2 \mathbf{- 20}x \mathbf{- 3}x + 5$ [product +60, sum −23]

$= 4x(3x - 5) - 1(3x - 5) = (3x - 5)(4x - 1)$

examiner's note To factorise a quadratic of the form $ax^2 + bx + c$, look for two numbers whose product is ac and whose sum is b.

Completing the square and using the quadratic formula

Q1 Write $x^2 + 4x - 3$ in the form $(x + a)^2 + b$

Q2 Write $x^2 - 3x + 7$ in the form $(x + a)^2 + b$

Q3 Solve $x^2 + 2x - 5 = 0$

Q4 Solve $3x^2 - 6x + 2 = 0$

ANSWERS

A1 $x^2 + 4x - 3 = (x + 2)^2 - 2^2 - 3 = (x + 2)^2 - 7$

A2 $x^2 - 3x + 7 = \left(x - \frac{3}{2}\right)^2 - \left(\frac{3}{2}\right)^2 + 7 = \left(x - \frac{3}{2}\right)^2 + \frac{19}{4}$

A3 $x = \frac{-2 \pm \sqrt{2^2 - 4 \times 1 \times (-5)}}{2} = \frac{-2 \pm \sqrt{24}}{2} \left[= -1 \pm \sqrt{6}\right]$

A4 $x = \frac{-(-6) \pm \sqrt{(-6)^2 - 4 \times 3 \times 2}}{2 \times 3} = \frac{6 \pm \sqrt{12}}{6} \left[= \frac{3 \pm \sqrt{3}}{3}\right]$

examiner's note Be extra careful with negative signs when using the quadratic formula.

Solving quadratic equations

Q1 Solve $(x + 1)(2x - 1) = 0$

Q2 Solve $x^2 - x - 2 = 0$

Q3 Solve $x(x - 3) = 10$

Q4 Solve $3x^2 - 2x - 7 = 0$

ANSWERS

A1 $(x + 1)(2x - 1) = 0 \Rightarrow (x + 1) = 0$ or $(2x - 1) = 0$

$\Rightarrow x = -1$ or $x = \frac{1}{2}$

A2 $x^2 - x - 2 = 0 \Rightarrow (x + 1)(x - 2) = 0 \Rightarrow x = -1$ or $x = 2$

A3 $x(x - 3) = 10 \Rightarrow x^2 - 3x - 10 = 0$

$\Rightarrow (x - 5)(x + 2) = 0 \Rightarrow x = 5$ or $x = -2$

A4 $3x^2 - 2x - 7 = 0$

$$\Rightarrow x = \frac{-(-2) \pm \sqrt{(-2)^2 - 4 \times 3 \times (-7)}}{2 \times 3} = \frac{2 \pm \sqrt{88}}{6}$$

$= 1.90$ or -1.23 (to 2 dp)

examiner's note Remember to always put the equation into the form 'quadratic expression = 0' before trying to solve it.

Solving simultaneous linear equations

Q1 Solve the simultaneous equations

$8x + 3y = 7$

$2x - y = 7$

Q2 Solve the simultaneous equations

$4x + 3y = 5$

$3x + 2y = 3$

Q3 Other than algebraically, how else can you solve simultaneous equations?

ANSWERS

A1 $8x + 3y = 7 \xrightarrow{\times 1} 8x + 3y = 7$

$2x - y = 7 \xrightarrow{\times 3} 6x - 3y = 21$

add $14x \qquad = 28$

so $x = 2$ and, from $2x - y = 7$, $y = 2 \times 2 - 7 = -3$
The solution is $x = 2$, $y = -3$

A2 $4x + 3y = 5 \xrightarrow{\times 2} 8x + 6y = 10$

$3x + 2y = 3 \xrightarrow{\times 3} 9x + 6y = 9$

subtract $-x \qquad = 1$

so $x = -1$ and, from $4x + 3y = 5$, $y = (5 - (-4))/3 = 3$
The solution is $x = -1$, $y = 3$

A3 Another way is to draw the graphs of the two equations and read off the coordinates of their point of intersection.

examiner's note Remember to give values for both x and y when stating the solution to simultaneous equations.

Solving simultaneous linear and quadratic equations

Q1 Solve the simultaneous equations

$x + y = -2$
$y = x^2 - 4x - 6$

Q2 Solve the simultaneous equations

$x + 3y = -8$
$x^2 + y^2 = 10$

ANSWERS

A1 $x + y = -2 \Rightarrow y = -x - 2$

$y = x^2 - 4x - 6 = -x - 2 \Rightarrow x^2 - 3x - 4 = 0$

$\Rightarrow (x - 4)(x + 1) = 0$

$\Rightarrow x = 4$ or $x = -1$

so $y = -6$ or $y = -1$

The solutions are $x = 4, y = -6$ and $x = -1, y = -1$

A2 $x + 3y = -8 \Rightarrow x = -8 - 3y$, so $x^2 = 64 + 48y + 9y^2$

Substituting this into $x^2 + y^2 = 10$ gives:

$64 + 48y + 9y^2 + y^2 = 10$

$10y^2 + 48y + 54 = 0$

$(10y + 18)(y + 3) = 0$

so $y = -1.8$ or $y = -3$, giving $x = -2.6$ or $x = 1$

The solutions are $x = -2.6, y = -1.8$ and $x = 1, y = -3$

examiner's note There will normally be **two pairs** of (x, y) values to find.

Algebraic fractions I

Q1 Simplify $\dfrac{3x+12}{x^2+4x}$

Q2 Write $\dfrac{3(x+2)}{4} \times \dfrac{8x}{x+2}$ as a single fraction in its lowest form.

Q3 Write $\dfrac{4x^2(x-2)}{3} \div \dfrac{2(x-2)}{x^3}$ as a single fraction in its lowest form.

Q4 Simplify $\dfrac{x^2-16}{x^2-2x-8}$

ANSWERS

A1 $\dfrac{3x+12}{x^2+4x} = \dfrac{3(x+4)}{x(x+4)} = \dfrac{3}{x}$

A2 $\dfrac{3(x+2)}{4} \times \dfrac{8x}{x+2} = \dfrac{24x(x+2)}{4(x+2)} = 6x$

A3 $\dfrac{4x^2(x-2)}{3} \div \dfrac{2(x-2)}{x^3} = \dfrac{4x^2(x-2)}{3} \times \dfrac{x^3}{2(x-2)} = \dfrac{2x^5}{3}$

A4 $\dfrac{x^2-16}{x^2-2x-8} = \dfrac{(x+4)(x-4)}{(x+2)(x-4)} = \dfrac{x+4}{x+2}$

***examiner's* note** Only complete expressions can be cancelled from top and bottom of an algebraic fraction — you must never cancel a term within an expression, such as the 'x's in the numerator and denominator of A4.

Algebraic fractions II

Q1 Write $\frac{4}{x} - \frac{3}{x-2}$ as a single fraction.

Q2 Write $\frac{3}{2x} - \frac{4}{5x^2}$ as a single fraction.

Q3 Solve $\frac{4}{x-1} + \frac{6}{5-x} = 5$

ANSWERS

A1 $\dfrac{4}{x} - \dfrac{3}{x-2} = \dfrac{4(x-2) - 3x}{x(x-2)} = \dfrac{x-8}{x(x-2)}$

A2 $\dfrac{3}{2x} - \dfrac{4}{5x^2} = \dfrac{15x}{10x^2} - \dfrac{8}{10x^2} = \dfrac{15x-8}{10x^2}$

A3 $\dfrac{4}{x-1} + \dfrac{6}{5-x} = 5 \Rightarrow 4(5-x) + 6(x-1) = 5(5-x)(x-1)$

$$\Rightarrow 20 - 4x + 6x - 6 = 25x - 5x^2 - 25 + 5x$$

$$\Rightarrow 5x^2 - 28x + 39 = 0$$

$$\Rightarrow (5x-13)(x-3) = 0, \text{ so } x = \frac{13}{5} \text{ or } x = 3$$

examiner's note You add and subtract algebraic fractions using the same principle as for arithmetic fractions, i.e. by taking a common denominator.

Transformations of graphs

Q1 Given the graph of $y = \mathrm{f}(x)$, describe how to get the graph of:

(a) $y = \mathrm{f}(x + 3)$

(b) $y = \mathrm{f}(x) + 3$

(c) $y = -\mathrm{f}(2x)$

Q2 Describe the second function (blue curve) on this graph in terms of f(x) (red curve).

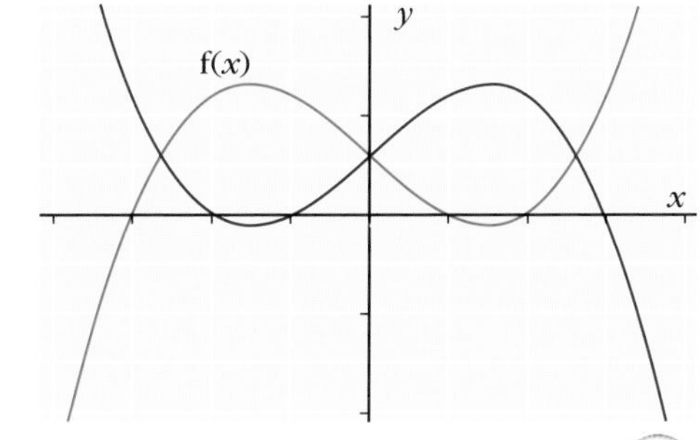

ANSWERS

A1 (a) Translation of 3 units to the left

(b) Translation of 3 units up

(c) A stretch by a factor of $\frac{1}{2}$ in the x-direction and a reflection in the x-axis

A2 The blue curve is the reflection of the red curve in the y-axis, so it is the graph of $f(-x)$.

examiner's note If the change is made to the x term **before** the function is applied, then the transformation is in the horizontal direction and has an opposite effect to what you might expect, e.g. $f(x + 3)$ is translation to the left and $f(2x)$ means stretching by a factor of $\frac{1}{2}$.

Transformations of trig graphs I

Q1 The graph of $y = \sin x$ is shown below. Sketch the graphs of:
(a) $y = 1 - \sin x$, (b) $y = -1 + 3\sin x$, (c) $y = 2\sin(x + 60)$

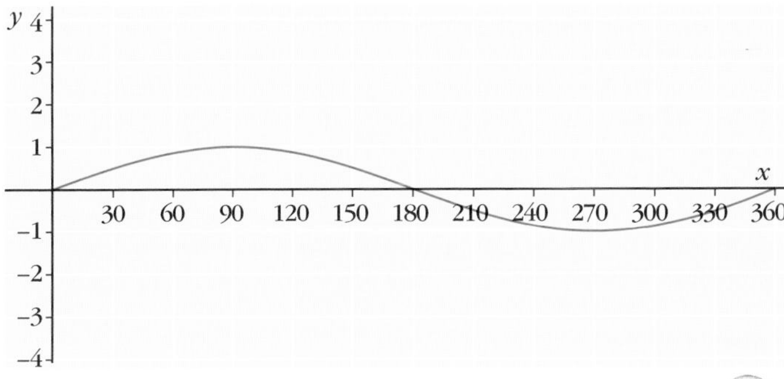

ANSWERS

A1

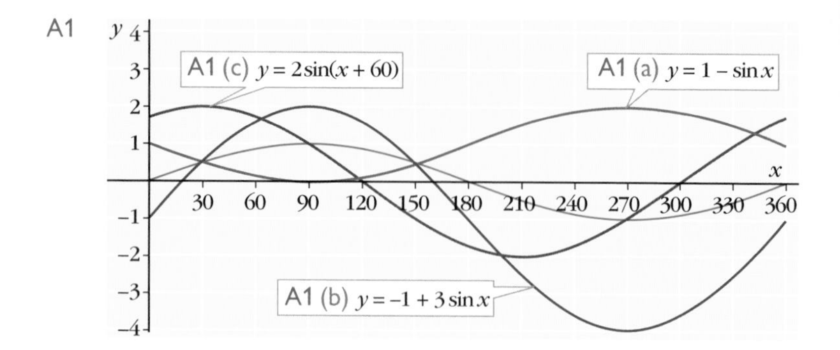

examiner's note You need to be able to recall the effects of different transformations quickly and accurately; otherwise, thinking through these effects can consume a lot of valuable time in the examination.

Transformations of trig graphs II

Q1 The graph of $y = a + b\cos x$ is shown below in red. Find the values of a and b.

Q2 The graph of $y = \tan(x - \theta)$ is shown below in green. Find the value of θ.

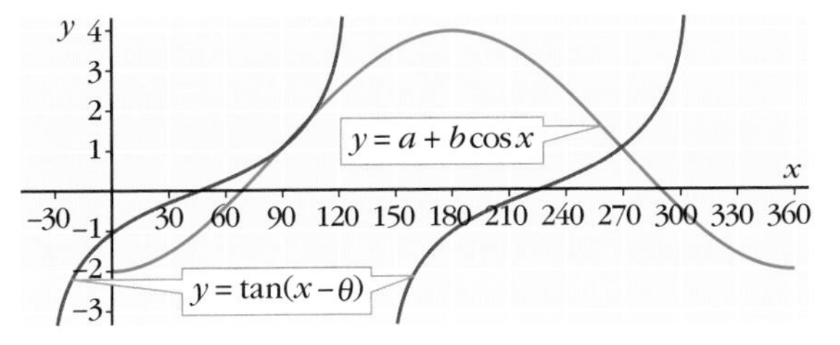

ANSWERS

A1 $a = 1$, $b = -3$.

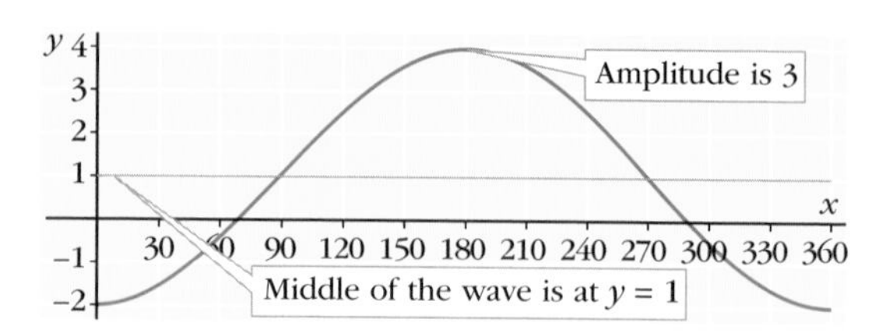

A2 $\tan 0 = 0$ and the graph has $y = 0$ at $x = 45$ (and 225), i.e. $\tan(45 - \theta) = 0$, so $\theta = 45$ (and 225).

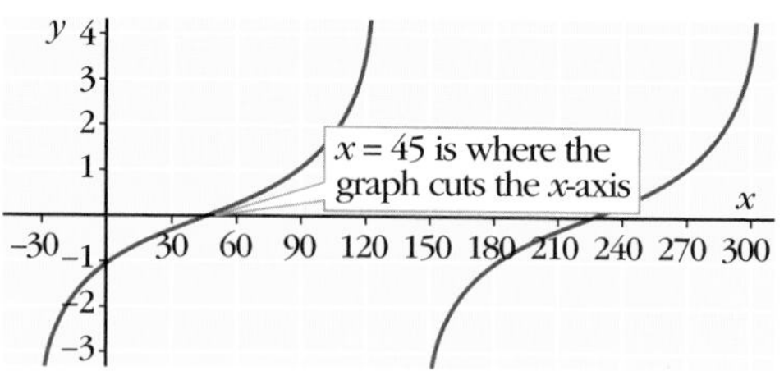

examiner's note The best starting point for working out the coefficients in a situation like Q1 is to find the constant term that is added to a sine or cosine wave.

Proof

Q1 Prove that half the sum of four consecutive integers must be odd.

Q2 (a) Verify that $n^2 - n + 41$ is prime for $n = 1, 2, 3$ and 4.

(b) Give a counter-example to prove that $n^2 - n + 41$ is not always prime. (Finding it 'by exhaustion', i.e. working through 5, 6, 7,... until you get a counter-example, is not a good idea!)

Q3 Prove that $6x + 7 < 4x - 3 + 2(x + 8)$ is an identity.

ANSWERS

A1 If n is the first of the four integers, then the others can be written as $n + 1$, $n + 2$ and $n + 3$. Adding these four numbers gives $4n + 6$. Half of this is $2n + 3$, which will be odd for any integer n.

A2 (a) The values of $n^2 - n + 41$ for $n = 1, 2, 3$ and 4 are 41, 43, 47 and 53, which are all prime.

(b) Taking $n = 41$ makes the second and third terms of the expression cancel each other, leaving just the squared term: $41^2 - 41 + 41 = 41^2$, which is a multiple of 41 and therefore not prime.

A3 $6x + 7 < 4x - 3 + 2(x + 8)$

$\Rightarrow 6x + 7 < 4x - 3 + 2x + 16$

$\Rightarrow 6x + 7 < 6x + 13$, which is always true for any value of x

examiner's note An inequality can be an identity — all that is required is that the statement be true for all values of x.

Area and perimeter of quadrilaterals

Q1 Find the area and perimeter of the quadrilateral ABCD. ∠ABD and ∠BCD are right angles

D
5cm
C
A
12cm
3cm
B

Q2 Find the area of the trapezium ABCD.

AB and DC are parallel

∠AED is a right angle

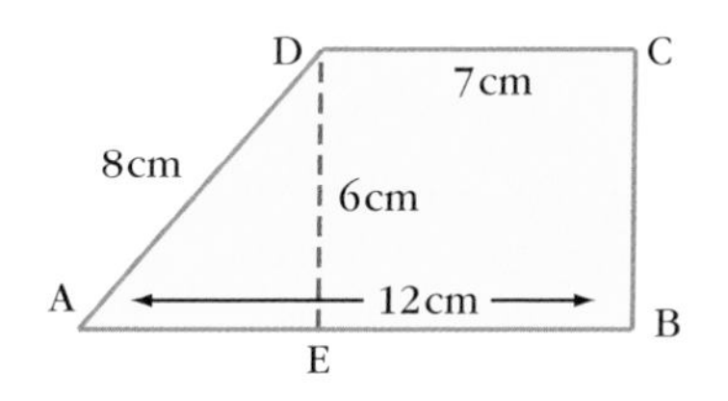

ANSWERS

A1 By Pythagoras' theorem, AD = 13 cm and CD = 4 cm

Perimeter of ABCD = 12 + 3 + 4 + 13 = 32 cm

Area of ABCD = area of ABD + area of BCD

$= \frac{1}{2} \times 12 \times 5 + \frac{1}{2} \times 3 \times 4 = 30 + 6 = 36\,\text{cm}^2$

A2 The area of a trapezium is the average of the parallel sides times the **perpendicular height**, which in this case is 6 cm

Area $= \frac{1}{2} \times (7 + 12) \times 6 = 57\,\text{cm}^2$

(Note that the length of AD is not needed in this calculation.)

examiner's note If you have to work out some lengths to put into a formula, you should show clearly where you got them from.

Angles in parallel lines

Q1 A is (–2, 1), B is (6, 7) and M is the midpoint of AB.

(a) Find the coordinates of M.

(b) Find the distance AB.

Q2 AB and CD are parallel lines. Find the angles x and y.

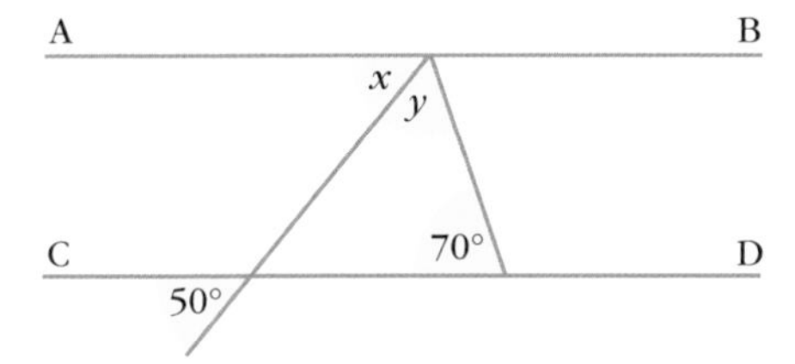

ANSWERS

A1 (a) The coordinates of the midpoint are found by taking the averages of the x- and y-coordinates of the endpoints. Here the average of –2 and 6 is 2, and the average of 1 and 7 is 4, so the midpoint is (2, 4).

(b) Using Pythagoras' theorem:

$AB^2 = (6 - (-2))^2 + (7 - 1)^2 = 8^2 + 6^2 = 100$, so $AB = 10$

A2 The angle marked as x and the angle marked as 50° are corresponding angles, so $x = 50°$

The third angle in the triangle is vertically opposite to the angle marked as 50°, so it is also 50°. Since the angle sum in a triangle is 180°, we have $50° + 70° + y = 180°$, so $y = 60°$

***examiner's* note** There are many different ways to work out y in Q2 — for example, you could use the fact that the third angle in the triangle is alternate to x, or that the third angle on the straight line with x and y is alternate to the angle marked as 70°. It does not matter which way you obtain the answer, as long as you explain clearly what you are doing.

Nets and projections

Q1 Draw a net for this cuboid.

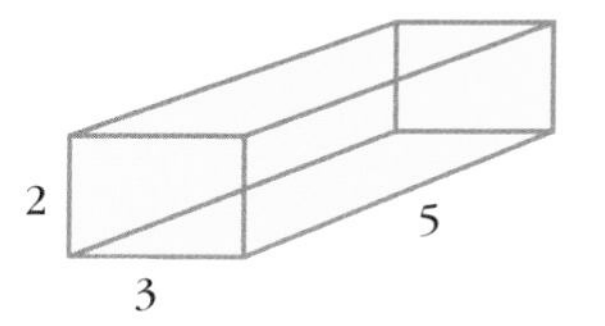

Q2 Draw the elevations of the following prism from directions A and B.

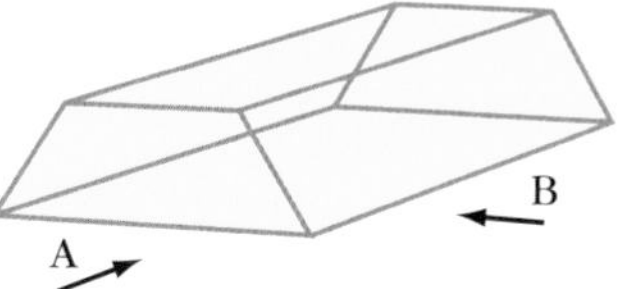

ANSWERS

A1

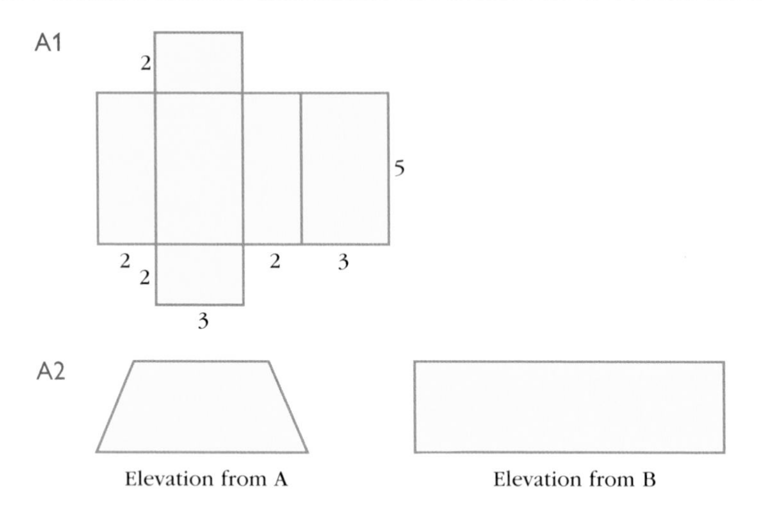

A2

examiner's note If lengths are given in a diagram, then you should label the corresponding lengths in the net or elevation.

Maps and scale drawings

Q1 Give the bearings of:

(a) B from A

(b) C from A

(c) D from A

(d) A from C

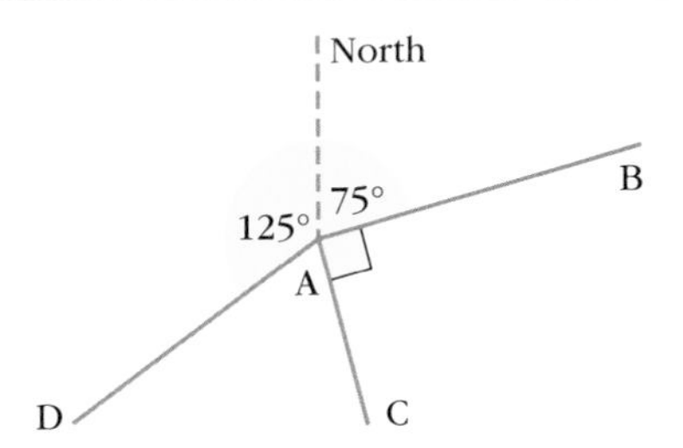

Q2 Town Q is 25 km from town P on a bearing of 125°.
Town R is 40 km from town P on a bearing of 265°.
Draw a sketch to show the positions of the three towns.

ANSWERS

A1 Bearings are always three-figure numbers measuring the angle turned from North in the clockwise direction.

(a) 075° (b) 75° + 90° = 165° (c) 360° – 125° = 235°

(d) If you draw in the North line at C, the line CA will make an angle of 15° with it, but in the **anticlockwise** direction. So the bearing is 360° – 15° = 345°

A2

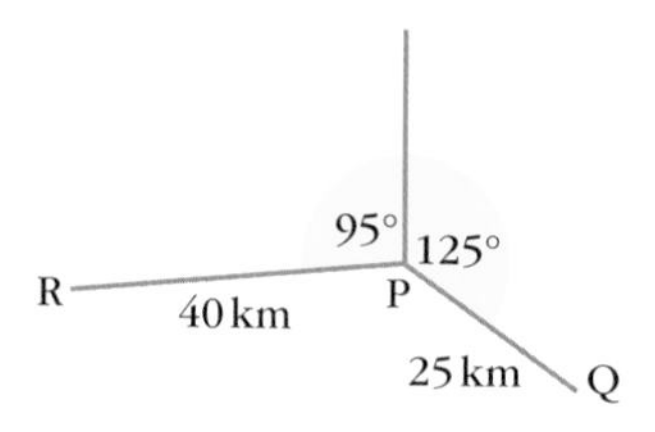

examiner's note If you have to do a scale drawing from given information as in Q2, it is worth making a rough sketch first to get an idea of what it should look like, and then do the accurate scale drawing.

Symmetry

Q1 The diagram shows a regular polygon.

(a) How many lines of symmetry does the figure have?

(b) What is the order of rotational symmetry of the figure?

Q2 How many planes of symmetry does this cuboid with square ends have?

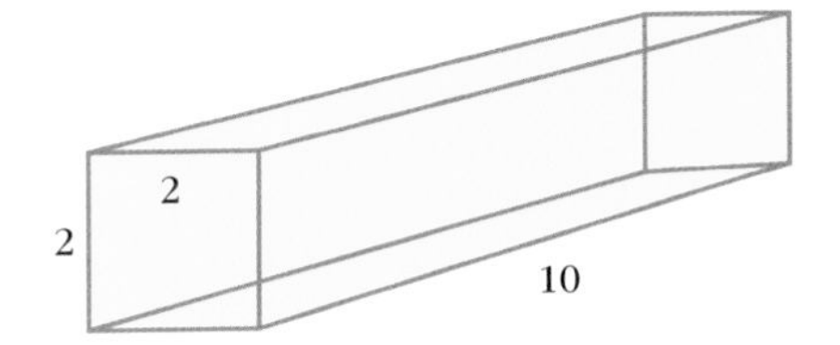

ANSWERS

A1 (a) 5 — the line joining each of the five vertices to the midpoint of the opposite side is a line of symmetry.

(b) 5 — the order of rotational symmetry is the number of times the shape would fit into its own outline during a single 360° turn; for any regular polygon, this will be the same as the number of vertices (and the number of sides).

A2 There is one plane of symmetry parallel to the square ends, halfway along the cuboid. There are four more planes that are perpendicular to the square ends (along the two diagonals and the two lines joining the midpoints of opposite sides of the square). So there are five planes of symmetry in total.

examiner's note Remember that a shape with no rotational symmetry must still be able to fit into its own outline once, so its order of rotational symmetry is 1.

Properties of triangles and quadrilaterals

Q1 Say whether each of the following statements is true or false, with a reason.

(a) All squares are rectangles.

(b) All rectangles are squares.

(c) Some kites are rhombuses.

(d) Some kites are rectangles.

Q2 (a) The angles in a triangle are in the ratio 3 : 2 : 2. What sort of triangle is it?

(b) Shape A is a quadrilateral whose diagonals bisect each other at right angles. What is the name for shape A?

ANSWERS

A1 (a) True — for a quadrilateral to be a rectangle, it needs only four right angles, and all squares have four right angles.
(b) False — a square is a special kind of rectangle, with all four sides having equal length.
(c) True — a kite is defined by two pairs of equal-length adjacent sides; only if these two pairs are also equal in length to each other will the kite be a rhombus.
(d) True – squares are kites that are also rectangles.

A2 (a) It is an isosceles triangle — the given ratio tells us that there is a pair of equal angles.
(b) Shape A is a rhombus. (A square's diagonals also bisect each other, but a rhombus is the most general shape with this property.)

examiner's note If you have to sketch a shape, try to make sure you draw it in the most general form possible, i.e. it does not have any extra properties. For example, check that a parallelogram you draw does not look as though all of its four sides are equal.

Properties of polygons

Q1 ABCDEFG is a convex polygon.

(a) What is the sum of the exterior angles of ABCDEFG?

(b) What is the sum of the interior angles of ABCDEFG?

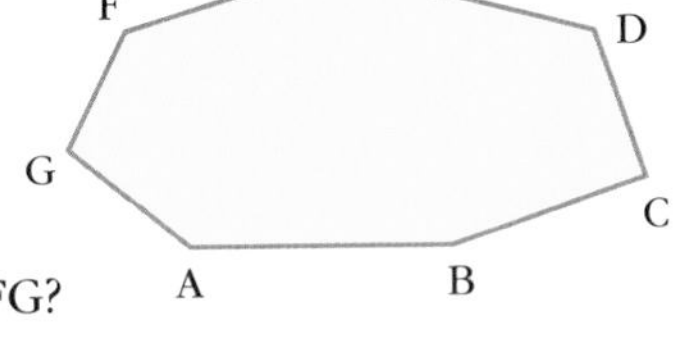

Q2 Find the value of x in the diagram (which is **not** drawn to scale).

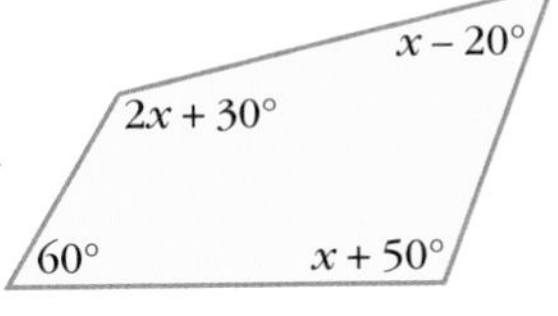

ANSWERS

A1 (a) 360° (The sum of exterior angles is always the same for any convex polygon.)

(b) 900° — ABCDEFG has seven sides, so the sum of the interior angles is $(7 - 2) \times 180° = 900°$

A2 $60° + (2x + 30°) + (x - 20°) + (x + 50°) = 360°$ (the angle sum in a quadrilateral)
i.e. $4x + 120° = 360°$, so $x = 60°$

examiner's note If you use a calculator, enter extra brackets to ensure that operations are performed in the correct order, or do the calculations in chunks as shown in the above solutions.

Rotations and reflections

Q1 Give the coordinates of the image of the point (4, 3) if triangle A is:

(a) reflected in the y-axis

(b) rotated 90° anticlockwise about the point (1, 0)

(c) reflected in the line $y = -x$

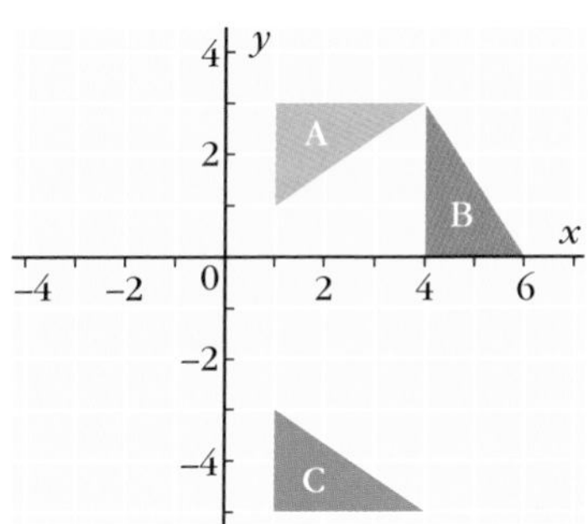

Q2 Describe the transformation that takes:

(a) A to B (b) A to C

ANSWERS

A1 (a) (−4, 3)

(b) (−2, 3)

(c) (−3, −4)

A2 (a) Rotation of 90° anticlockwise about the point (4, 3)

(b) Reflection in the line $y = -1$

examiner's note When working with transformations, especially rotations, you may find it helpful to use tracing paper.

Translations and enlargements

Q1 Describe the transformations that take:

(a) triangle A to triangle B
(b) triangle A to triangle C
(c) triangle B to triangle A
(d) triangle C to triangle B

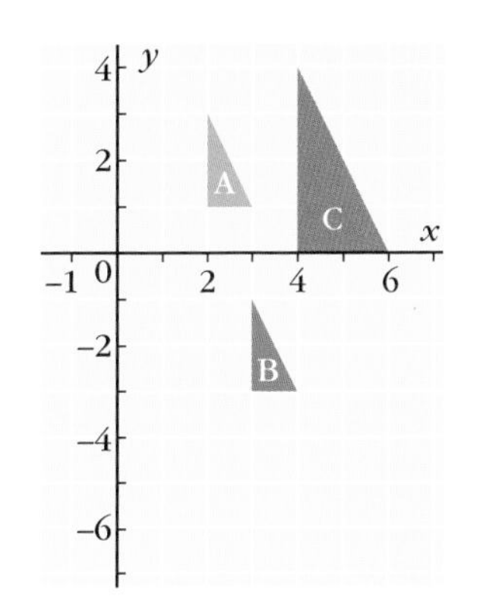

ANSWERS

A1

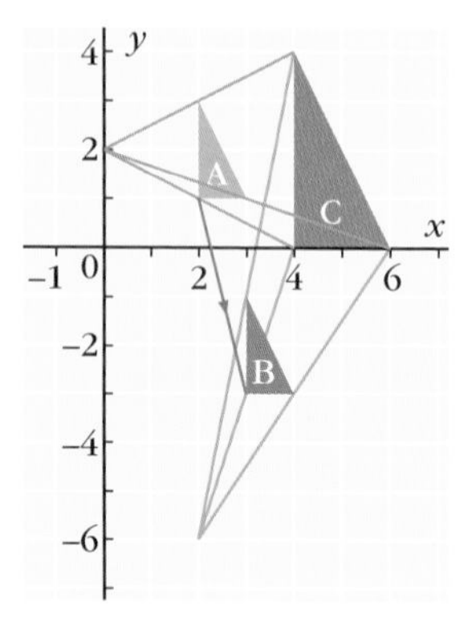

(a) Translation by vector $\begin{pmatrix} 1 \\ -4 \end{pmatrix}$.

(b) Enlargement by factor 2 with centre (0, 2).

(c) Translation by vector $\begin{pmatrix} -1 \\ 4 \end{pmatrix}$.

(d) Enlargement by scale factor $\frac{1}{2}$ with centre (2, –6).

***examiner's* note** When working with enlargements, it helps to draw in the lines passing through the centres and/or corresponding vertices of the original shape and its image.

Combining transformations

Q1 B is the image of A under a rotation of 90° clockwise about the origin. C is a reflection of B in the x-axis. D is a reflection of C in the y-axis.

(a) Describe the single transformation that takes A onto C.

(b) Describe the single transformation that takes B onto D.

(c) Describe the single transformation that takes A onto D.

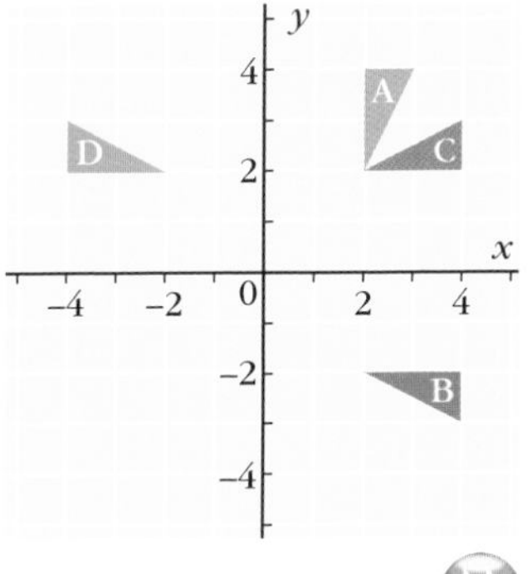

ANSWERS

A1 (a) Reflection in the line $y = x$.

(b) Rotation of 180° about the origin.

(c) Rotation of 90° anticlockwise about the origin.

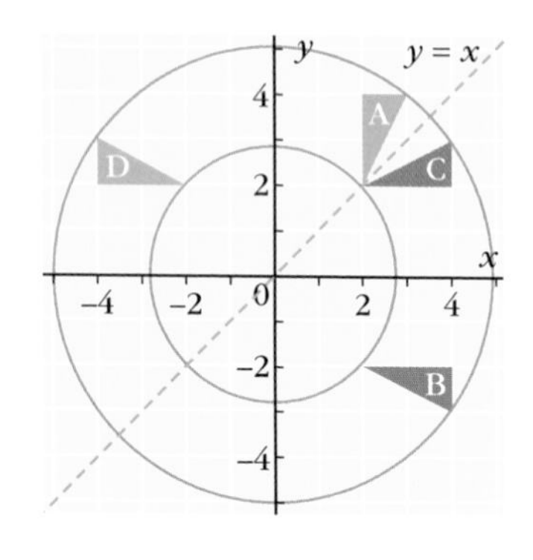

examiner's note The order in which transformations are applied can be important, so always do them in the order given.

Compound measures

Q1 Katrina travels for 30 minutes at an average speed of 32 miles per hour (mph) and then for one and a half hours on the motorway at an average speed of 68 mph. Work out her average speed over the journey.

Q2 Gold has a density of $19.3\,g/cm^3$. What will be the mass of a small rectangular bar of gold that is 2 cm by 1.5 cm by 1 cm?

Q3 Amjan's car averages 20 kilometres per litre of diesel. Diesel costs 108.9p per litre. If Amjan drives his car on a journey of 180 km, how much will the diesel cost?

ANSWERS

A1 Katrina travels $32 \times 0.5 = 16$ miles in the first half hour, and then $68 \times 1.5 = 102$ miles in the next one and a half hours. Altogether she travels 118 miles in 2 hours, so the average speed is $118 \div 2 = 59$ mph.

A2 Mass = density × volume. The bar has a volume of $2\,\text{cm} \times 1.5\,\text{cm} \times 1\,\text{cm} = 3\,\text{cm}^3$, so its mass is $19.3\,\text{g/cm}^3 \times 3\,\text{cm}^3 = 57.9$ grams.

A3 On a journey of 180 km Amjan will use about 9 litres of diesel. The cost will be 108.9p/litre × 9 litres = 980.1p or £9.80.

examiner's note Writing down brief comments on what you are working out can be very helpful in keeping track of what the calculations are telling you — later on you might need to go back and reuse some of the information.

Areas and volumes I

Q1 Find the surface area and the volume of the cuboid shown.

2 m
7 m
4 m

Q2 Find the surface area and the volume of the triangular prism shown.

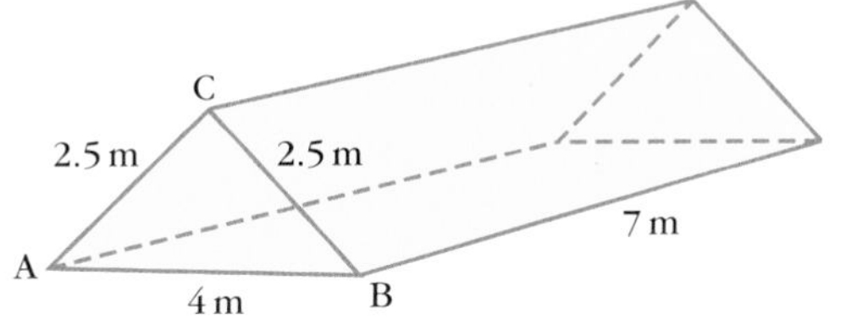

ANSWERS

A1 Volume $= 7\,\text{m} \times 4\,\text{m} \times 2\,\text{m} = 56\,\text{m}^3$

The surface of the cuboid is made up of three pairs of rectangular faces, which are 4 m by 7 m, 4 m by 2 m and 7 m by 2 m.
Surface area $= 2 \times (4 \times 7 + 4 \times 2 + 7 \times 2) = 100\,\text{m}^2$

A2 The perpendicular height h of the isosceles triangle ABC can be found by Pythagoras' theorem: $2^2 + h^2 = 2.5^2 \Rightarrow h = 1.5$. So the area of ABC is $\frac{1}{2} \times 4 \times 1.5 = 3\,\text{m}^2$
Volume of prism $= 3\,\text{m}^2 \times 7\,\text{m} = 21\,\text{m}^3$

The surface of the prism is made up of two triangles (ABC and another identical one) and three rectangular faces.
Surface area $= 2 \times 3\,\text{m}^2 + 4\,\text{m} \times 7\,\text{m} + 2.5\,\text{m} \times 7\,\text{m} + 2.5\,\text{m} \times 7\,\text{m}$
$= 69\,\text{m}^2$

examiner's note In questions like these, you will often need to work out quantities such as heights before you can move on to calculate the areas and/or volumes asked for.

Areas and volumes II

Q1 Find the volume and total surface area of the cone shown. Give your answers as exact values.

Q2 A solid hemisphere has a radius of 6 cm. Give the volume and surface area of the hemisphere as exact values.

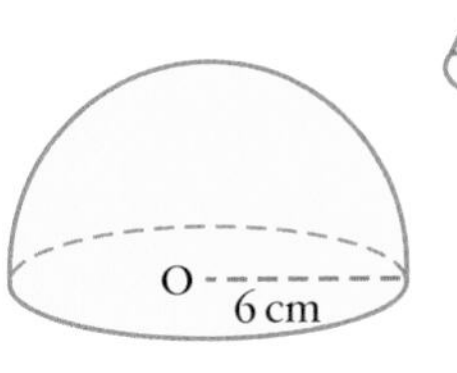

A1 By Pythagoras' theorem, the slant height of the cone is 13 cm

Volume $= \frac{1}{3}\pi r^2 h = \frac{1}{3}\pi \times 5^2 \times 12 = 100\pi\ \text{cm}^3$

Surface area = area of base + curved surface area
$= \pi r^2 + \pi r l = \pi \times 5^2 + \pi \times 5 \times 13 = 25\pi + 65\pi = 90\pi\ \text{cm}^2$

A2 A sphere has volume $\frac{4}{3}\pi r^3$ and surface area $4\pi r^2$.
The volume of a hemisphere is just half that of the sphere:
$\frac{2}{3}\pi r^3 = \frac{2}{3}\pi \times 6^3 = 144\pi\ \text{cm}^3$

The surface area of the hemisphere is half that of the sphere plus the area of the flat circular face:
$2\pi r^2 + \pi r^2 = 3\pi \times 6^2 = 108\pi\ \text{cm}^2$

examiner's note Even if you are asked to give the final answer in decimal format, it is a good idea to keep calculated quantities as multiples of π for as long as possible, to avoid introducing rounding errors in intermediate calculations.

Written communication in geometry

Q1 The diagram shows a net which is a sector of a circle used to make a cone.

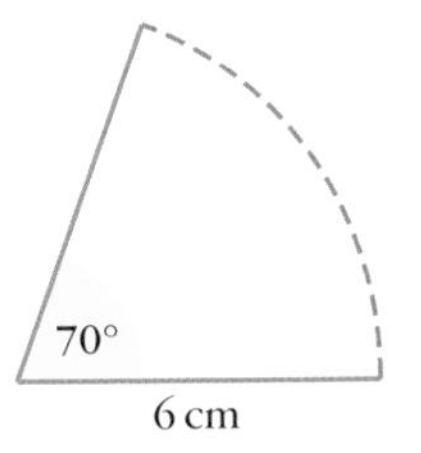

Calculate the vertical height of the cone, giving your answer as an exact value.

A1 The arc length of the sector will be the circumference of the base of the cone, and the radius of the sector will be the slant height of the cone.

Let r = radius of the base of cone; then $\frac{70}{360} \times 2\pi \times 6 = 2\pi r$,

so $r = \frac{7}{6}$

Let h = vertical height of the cone; then $h^2 + r^2 = 6^2$,

i.e. $h^2 + \left(\frac{7}{6}\right)^2 = 36$

so $h = \sqrt{36 - \left(\frac{7}{6}\right)^2} = \frac{\sqrt{1247}}{6}$

examiner's note When asked to give exact answers, be particularly careful to show the development of your solutions clearly. This is the sort of question that can be used to assess written communication in geometry.

Circle area and circumference

Q1 Find the perimeter and area of the sector shown.

12 cm

50°

Q2 A courtyard that is 10 m by 12 m has a spotlight in each of its four corners which lights up a sector with radius 8 m.

(a) If only one of the spotlights is working, what percentage of the courtyard will be lit?

(b) If all four spotlights are working, will the whole courtyard be lit?

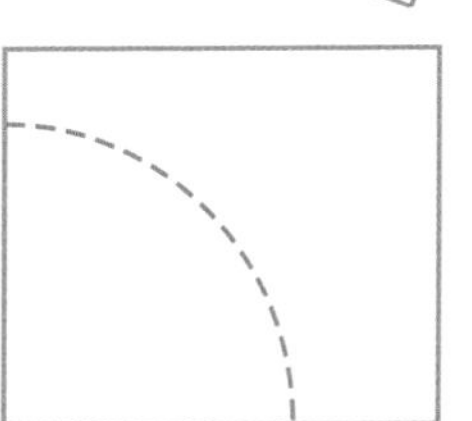

ANSWERS

A1 The arc length is $\frac{50}{360} \times 2\pi \times 12\,\text{cm} = \frac{10}{3}\pi\,\text{cm}$

Perimeter $= \frac{10}{3}\pi + 2 \times 12 = 34.5\,\text{cm}$ (to 3 sf)

Area $= \frac{50}{360} \times \pi \times 12^2 = 20\pi = 62.8\,\text{cm}^2$ (to 3 sf)

A2 (a) The area lit is $\frac{1}{4} \times \pi \times 8^2 = 16\pi\,\text{m}^2$.

The total area of the courtyard is $10 \times 12 = 120\,\text{m}^2$,

so the percentage lit is $\frac{16\pi}{120} \times 100\% = 41.9\%$ (to 3 sf).

(b) If the diagonals of the courtyard are 16 m or shorter, the illumination from each spotlight will reach at least halfway along one of the diagonals and the whole courtyard will be lit. The diagonal has length $\sqrt{10^2 + 12^2} = 15.6\,\text{m}$, so the courtyard will all be lit.

examiner's note First identify arcs and sectors by their angle and the fraction of the circle they account for; then calculating areas and perimeters will follow easily.

Circle properties

Q1 T is a point outside a circle whose centre is C.
TA and TB are the tangents to the circle from T.
Explain why TACB is a kite.

Q2 C is the centre of a circle with radius 4 cm.
AB is a chord which is 3 cm long.
Find the area of the minor segment cut off by AB.

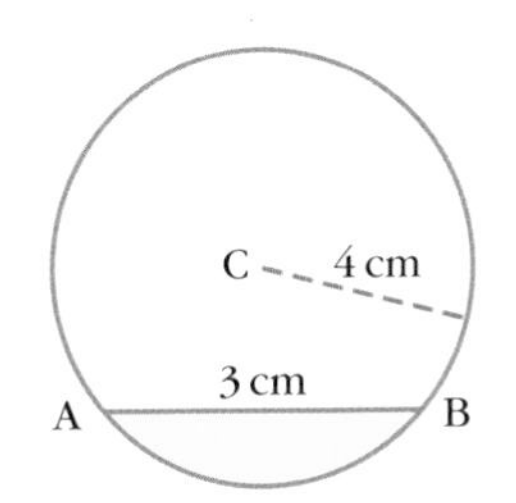

ANSWERS

A1 The two tangents from a point to a circle are of equal length, i.e. TA = TB. AC and BC are both radii. Two pairs of equal adjacent sides $\Rightarrow$ TACB is a kite.

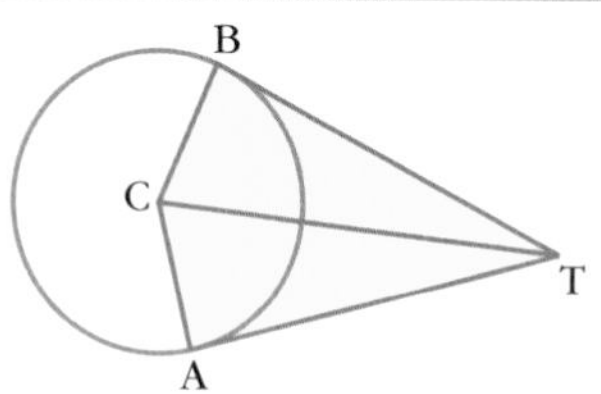

A2 The area of the segment is the area of the sector less the area of the triangle.

First we need to find the angle θ at the centre:

$\sin\left(\frac{\theta}{2}\right) = \frac{1.5}{4} \Rightarrow \theta = 44.0°$

Let h be the height of the triangle; then $1.5^2 + h^2 = 4^2$, so $h = 3.71$

Area of segment $= \frac{44.0}{360} \times \pi \times 4^2 - \frac{1}{2} \times 3 \times 3.71$

$= 6.1435... - 5.562... = 0.58$ (to 2 sf)

examiner's note Remember that when working with circles, you get lots of equal lengths (especially radii).

Circle theorems I

Q1 Prove that the angle in a semicircle is 90°.

Q2 Find angle ADC in the diagram. Give reasons for your answer.

B
O
A
110°
D
C

Q3 AOBC is a straight line where O is the centre of the circle.
BC = BD and ∠BCD = 25°.
Find angle BAD.

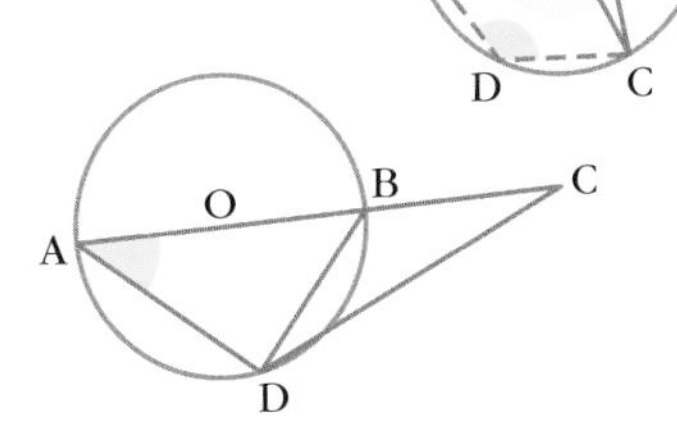

ANSWERS

A1 OAC and OBC are isoceles triangles.

$2x + 2y = 180°$

$\Rightarrow \angle ACB = x + y = 90°$.

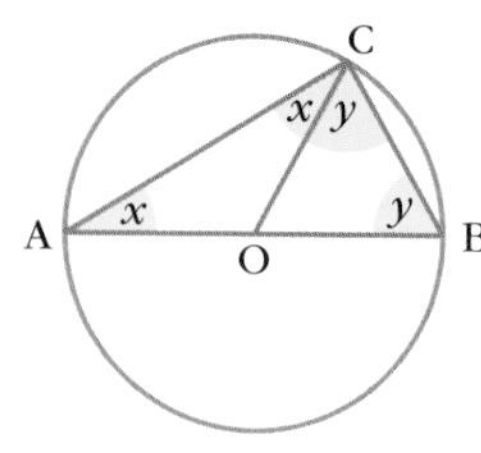

A2 $\angle AOC = 2\angle ABC$, so $\angle ABC = 55°$

$\angle ABC + \angle ADC = 180°$, so $\angle ADC = 125°$

A3 In isosceles triangle BCD, $\angle DBC + 25° + 25° = 180°$, so $\angle DBC = 130°$. Hence $\angle ABD = 50°$.

We know that $\angle ADB = 90°$ since it is the angle in a semicircle, so $\angle BAD = 40°$

examiner's note With problems involving circle theorems, the best approach may not always be obvious. So be prepared to go through the different theorems in turn and work out as much additional information as you can, until you can see how to get what is asked for.

Circle theorems II

Q1 Find angle APB in the diagram.

Q2 ST is a tangent to the circle at C. Prove that AB is a diameter.

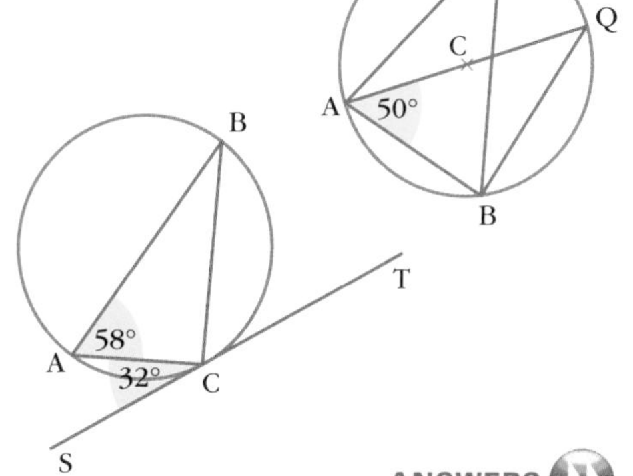

ANSWERS

A1 Since line ACQ is a diameter, $\angle ABQ = 90°$ and hence $\angle AQB = 40°$.
Then $\angle APB = 40°$ as well, because it is standing on the same arc as $\angle AQB$.

A2 The alternate segment theorem tells us that:
$\angle BCT = \angle BAC = 58°$ and $\angle CBA = \angle ACS = 32°$

Then angles in a triangle ($\angle CBA + \angle BAC + \angle ACB$) or angles on a straight line ($\angle BCT + \angle ACB + \angle ACS$) give $\angle ACB = 90°$, so AB must be a diameter (an angle in a semicircle is a right angle).

examiner's note Remember that you cannot assume that a chord is a diameter unless you are given something specific (such as the centre of the circle being marked on it) or you can deduce it from other information (such as a right angle at the circumference, like in A2).

Constructions

Q1 Construct the angle bisector of ∠ABC below.

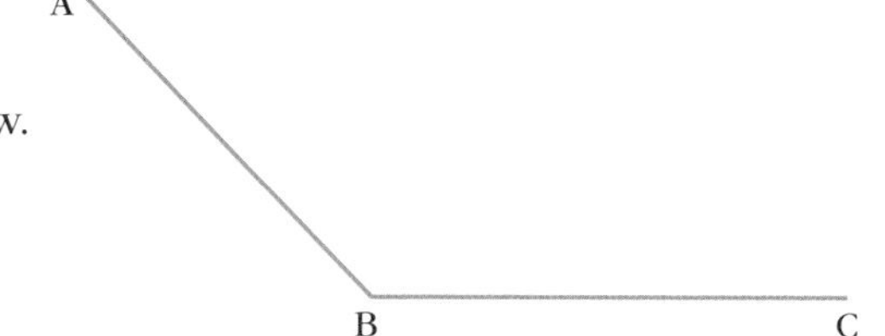

Q2 Construct the perpendicular bisector of AB.

A B

A1 Mark equal arcs from B on the two legs BA and BC, and label as P and Q. Next, draw equal arcs from P and Q, and label their intersection X. The line BX is the angle bisector of ∠ABC.

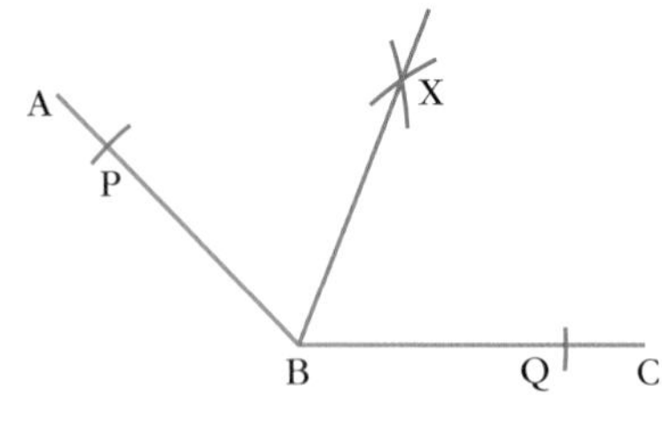

A2 Draw equal arcs on either side of AB (above and below the line) from A and from B; mark the two intersections of these arcs. Join the points of intersection to give the perpendicular bisector of AB.

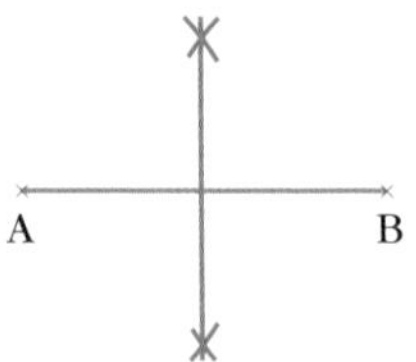

examiner's note Make sure you show construction marks such as arcs clearly — do not rub them out after completing the construction. It would be helpful also if you could describe briefly in words what you have done.

Similar figures

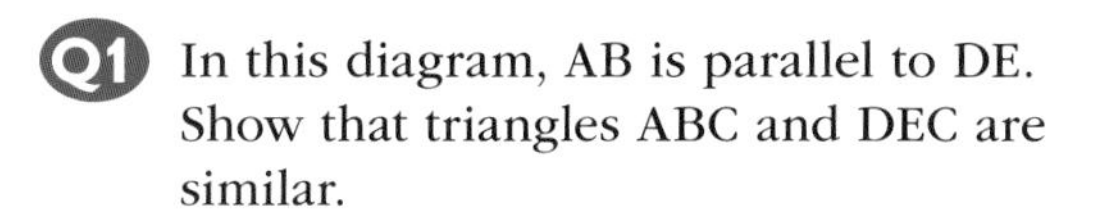

Q1 In this diagram, AB is parallel to DE. Show that triangles ABC and DEC are similar.

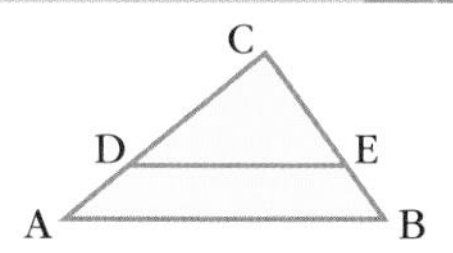

Q2 ABCD are points on the circumference of a circle with centre O.
AC and BD intersect at X.
AB = 8 cm, BX = 12 cm, DX = 7 cm,
DC = 4 cm.
Show that triangles ABX and DCX are similar. Find the lengths of CX and AX.
(The diagram is not drawn to scale.)

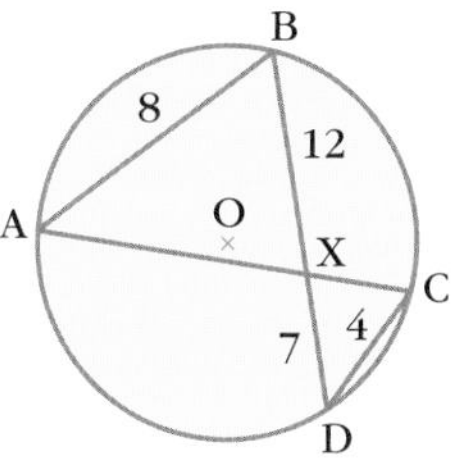

ANSWERS

A1 Since DE is parallel to AB, $\angle CAB$ and $\angle CDE$ are corresponding angles, hence $\angle CAB = \angle CDE$
Likewise, $\angle ABC = \angle DEC$
Also, $\angle ACB = \angle DCE$ (they are the same angle)
Therefore triangles ABC and DEC are similar because all of their angles are equal.

A2 $\angle ABD = \angle ACD$ because they are angles standing on the same arc. Likewise, $\angle CDB = \angle CAB$.
$\angle AXB = \angle CXD$ because they are vertically opposite angles.
Therefore triangles ABX and DCX are similar because all of their angles are equal.
The ratio of corresponding sides is $AB : DC = 2 : 1$
so $CX = BX/2 = 6$ cm and $AX = 2\,DX = 14$ cm

examiner's note When doing calculations with similar triangles, it can be helpful to draw the two triangles beside each other with the same orientation, to help identify corresponding sides.

Congruence

Q1 Explain whether the triangles shown are congruent.

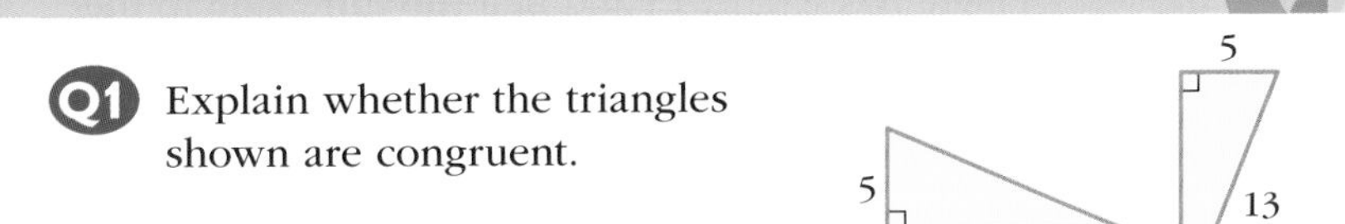

Q2 The two triangles below are congruent. Find the lengths of AB and PQ.

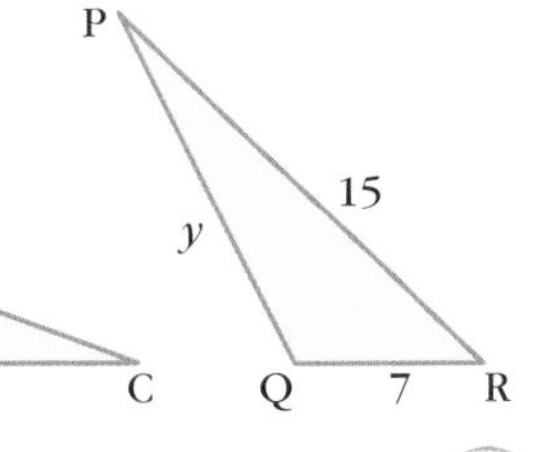

ANSWERS

A1 Given that the triangles are right-angled, we can use Pythagoras' theorem to work out that the hypotenuse in the left triangle has length 13 and that the third side in the right triangle has length 12. So the triangles are congruent because the three sides of each all have the same lengths as the three sides of the other.

A2 Given that the triangles are congruent, their three sides must have the same three lengths. Since AC = PR = 15, we must have $x = 7$ and $y = 13$.

***examiner's* note** Congruence requires exactly the same size and shape of figure, but the orientation does not have to be the same, so two figures can be turned around or even flipped over relative to each other and still be congruent.

Pythagoras' theorem

Q1 The sides of a triangle are 12 cm, 8 cm and 14 cm. Show that the triangle is not right-angled.

Q2 In the figure, AB = 5 cm and BC = 13 cm. D is the midpoint of AC. Find the distance BD.

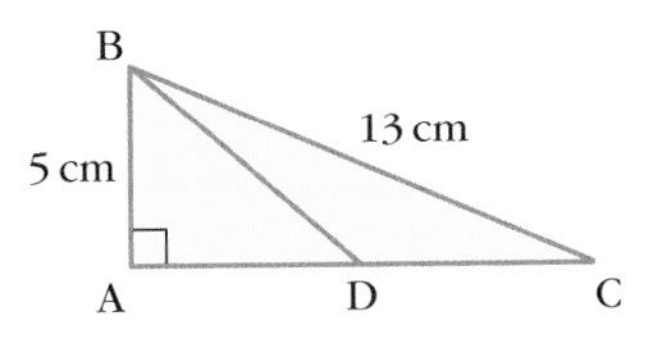

Q3 A rectangular room is 5 metres long, 4 metres wide and 3.5 metres high. Find the furthest distance between any two points in the room.

ANSWERS

A1 $14^2 = 196$; $12^2 + 8^2 = 144 + 64 = 208$. Since the square on the longest side is not equal to the sum of the other two squares, the triangle cannot be right-angled.

A2 By Pythagoras' theorem, AC = 12 cm, so AD = 6 cm
$BD^2 = AB^2 + AD^2 = 5^2 + 6^2 = 61$, so $BD = \sqrt{61} = 7.81$ cm (to 3 sf)

A3 The furthest distance d between any two points in a cuboid is the length of the space diagonal:
$d = \sqrt{5^2 + 4^2 + 3.5^2} = \sqrt{53.25} = 7.30$ m (to 3 sf)

examiner's note It is not very helpful to remember Pythagoras' theorem as $a^2 = b^2 + c^2$, because problems will rarely have a, b and c in them. A good way to remember the theorem is verbally: 'the square on the hypotenuse = the sum of the other two squares' — this form does not depend on how information is given in the question.

Trigonometry

Q1 Find x.

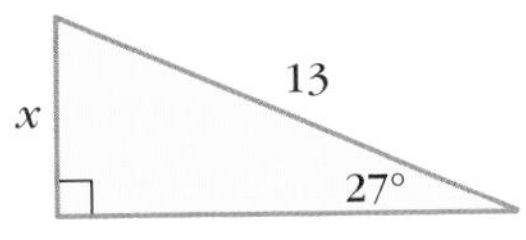

Q2 Find θ.

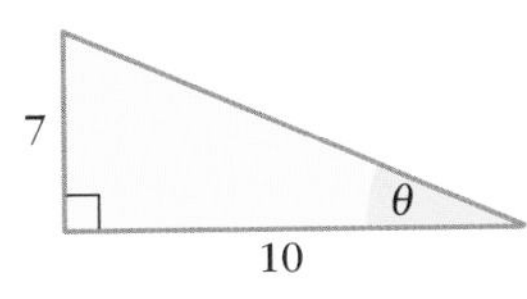

Q3 Find p.

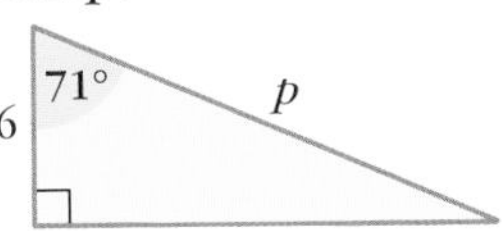

Q4 Find the angle that DF makes with the plane ABFE.

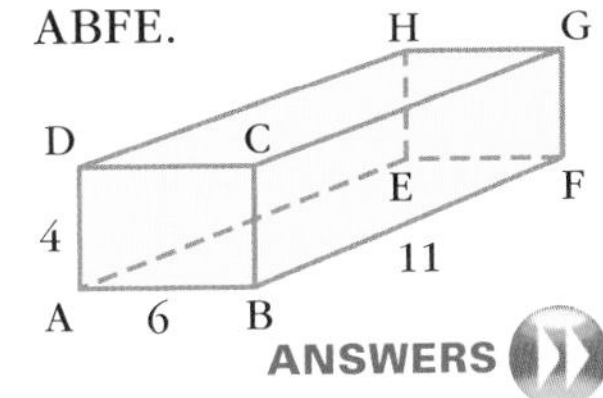

ANSWERS

A1 $\sin 27^\circ = \dfrac{x}{13} \Rightarrow x = 13 \sin 27^\circ = 5.90$ (to 3 sf)

A2 $\tan\theta = \dfrac{7}{10} \qquad \theta = \tan^{-1}(0.7) = 35.0^\circ$ (to 3 sf)

A3 $\cos 71^\circ = \dfrac{6}{p} \Rightarrow p = \dfrac{6}{\cos 71^\circ} = 18.4$ (to 3 sf)

A4 The angle required is ∠DFA, and in triangle DFA there is a right angle at ∠DAF. By Pythagoras' theorem applied to triangle ABF, $AF = \sqrt{6^2 + 11^2} = 12.52996\ldots$, so in triangle DFA, $\tan \angle DFA = \dfrac{DA}{AF} = \dfrac{4}{12.529964\ldots} = 0.3192\ldots$ and hence $\angle DFA = 17.70^\circ$ (to 3 sf).

examiner's note When you have a right-angled triangle in the question, use Pythagoras' theorem or the definitions of sin, cos and tan to solve the problem (rather than the sine or cosine rules).

Sine and cosine rules

Q1 Find the angle Q and the length of the side PQ.

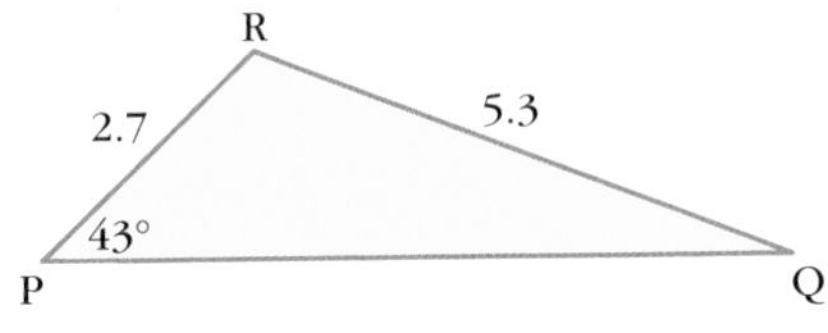

Q2 Find the length of the side QR and the angles Q and R.

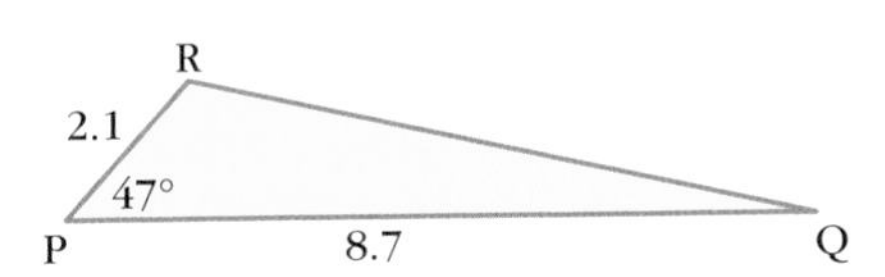

ANSWERS

A1 $\frac{\sin Q}{2.7} = \frac{\sin 43°}{5.3} \Rightarrow \sin Q = 2.7 \times \frac{\sin 43°}{5.3} = 0.3474\ldots$

so $Q = \sin^{-1}(0.3474\ldots) = 20.3°$

The angle $R = 180° - (43° + 20.3°) = 116.7°$

$\frac{\text{PQ}}{\sin 116.7°} = \frac{5.3}{\sin 43°} \Rightarrow \text{PQ} = \sin 116.7° \times \frac{5.3}{\sin 43°} = 6.94$ (to 3 sf)

A2 $\text{RQ}^2 = 2.1^2 + 8.7^2 - 2 \times 2.1 \times 8.7 \cos 47° = 55.179\ldots$

so $\text{RQ} = 7.4283\ldots = 7.43$ (to 3 sf)

$\frac{\sin Q}{2.1} = \frac{\sin 47°}{7.4283\ldots} \Rightarrow \sin Q = 2.1 \times \frac{\sin 47°}{7.4283\ldots} = 0.20675\ldots$

$Q = \sin^{-1}(0.20675\ldots) = 11.9°$ (to 1 dp), $R = 121.1°$

examiner's note If you have to work out an angle from three sides, find the largest angle first (opposite the longest side) using the cosine rule — this way you will pick up any obtuse angle if there is one. When using the sine rule, leave the largest angle till last.

Sine and cosine rules and area of a triangle

Q1 A triangle has sides of length 5.7 cm, 6.1 cm and 9.2 cm.

(a) Find the size of the angles in the triangle.

(b) Find the area of the triangle.

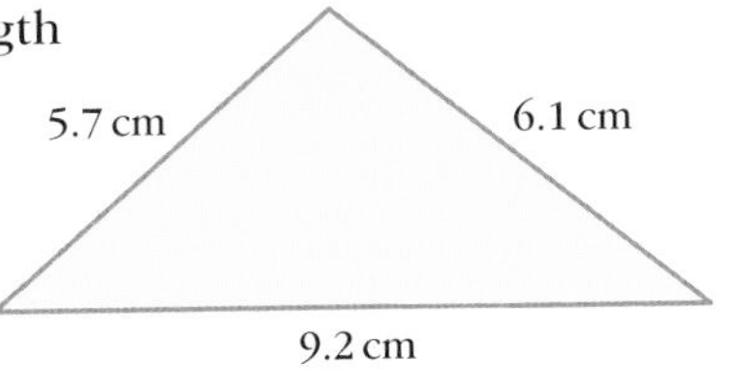

Q2 In triangle ABC, AB = 24.3 cm, $\angle BAC = 52.1°$ and BC = 21.1 cm. Find the two possible angles ACB and the two possible lengths of AC.

ANSWERS

A1 (a) The largest angle is always opposite the longest side:

$9.2^2 = 5.7^2 + 6.1^2 - 2 \times 5.7 \times 6.1 \cos\theta$

$$\Rightarrow \cos\theta = \frac{5.7^2 + 6.1^2 - 9.2^2}{2 \times 5.7 \times 6.1} \Rightarrow \theta = 102.4°$$

$$\frac{\sin\alpha}{6.1} = \frac{\sin 102.4°}{9.2} \Rightarrow \sin\alpha = 6.1 \times \frac{\sin 102.4°}{9.2} \Rightarrow \alpha = 40.4°$$

For the third angle: $180° - 102.4° - 40.4° = 37.2°$

(b) Area $= \frac{1}{2} \times 5.7 \times 6.1 \times \sin 102.4° = 17.0\,\text{cm}^2$

A2 $$\frac{\sin C}{24.3} = \frac{\sin 52.1°}{21.1} \Rightarrow \sin C = 0.90875\ldots \Rightarrow C = 65.3°$$

or $180° - 65.3° = 114.7°$

Hence $B = 62.6°$ or $13.2°$

and then $$\frac{\text{AC}}{\sin B} = \frac{21.1}{\sin 52.1°} \Rightarrow \text{AC} = 23.7 \text{ or } 6.11$$

examiner's note When you know all three sides or two sides and the angle between them, only the cosine rule is needed.

Proofs and problems involving sine and cosine rules

Q1 A helicopter has flown 27 km on a bearing of 140° when it answers an emergency call. It then flies 15 km on a bearing of 056° to pick up an injured climber. How far is the helicopter from its base, and on what bearing does it need to fly to get back to base?

Q2 Prove that $\frac{\sin A}{a} = \frac{\sin B}{b}$ in the triangle shown.

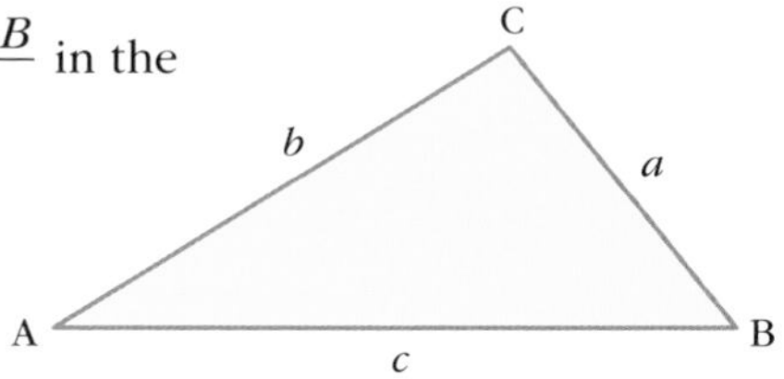

C
b
a
A
B
c

ANSWERS

A1 $x^2 = 27^2 + 15^2 - 2 \times 27 \times 15 \cos 96°$,
so $x = 32.2$ km

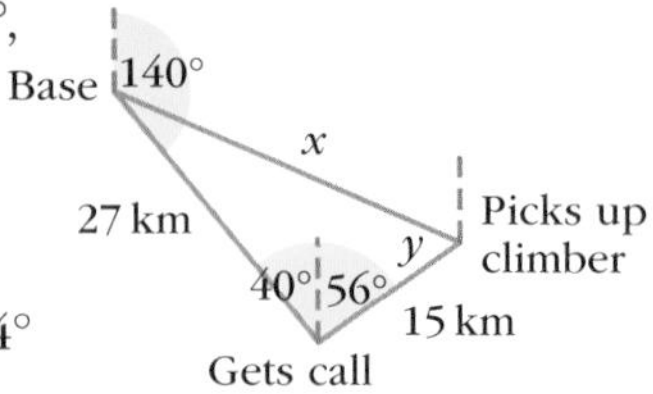

$$\frac{\sin y}{27} = \frac{\sin 96°}{32.228\ldots}$$

$$\Rightarrow y = \sin^{-1}\left(27 \times \frac{\sin 96°}{32.228\ldots}\right) = 56.4°$$

Base, 140°, x, 27 km, Picks up climber, y, 40°, 56°, 15 km, Gets call

so to return to base the helicopter has to fly on a bearing of $180° + 56° + 56.4° = 292.4°$

A2 Suppose the perpendicular from C onto AB meets AB at point P, and that h is the height CP:

$$\sin A = \frac{h}{b} \quad \text{and} \quad \sin B = \frac{h}{a}$$

hence $h = b \sin A = a \sin B$, so $\dfrac{\sin A}{a} = \dfrac{\sin B}{b}$

examiner's note If you find a right-angled triangle in the problem, it will be much easier to use basic trigonometry than the sine and cosine rules.

Graphs of trig functions

Q1 Write down the key features of the graph of $y = \sin x$ and sketch the graph.

Q2 Write down the key features of the graph of $y = \tan x$ and sketch the graph.

Q3 One solution to the equation $(\sin x)^2 = 0.25$ is $x = 30°$. Give all the other solutions in the range 0 to 360°.

Q4 One solution to the equation $(\tan x)^3 = -0.125$ is $x = 172.9°$. Give all the other solutions in the range 0 to 360°.

ANSWERS

A1 Sine is a wave function with period 360°. The graph goes through the origin and oscillates between –1 and 1.

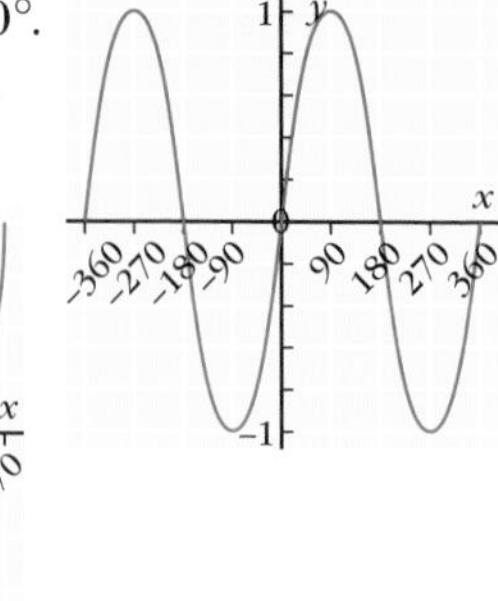

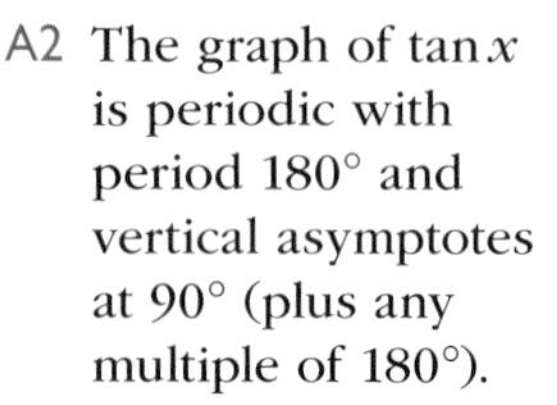

A2 The graph of $\tan x$ is periodic with period 180° and vertical asymptotes at 90° (plus any multiple of 180°).

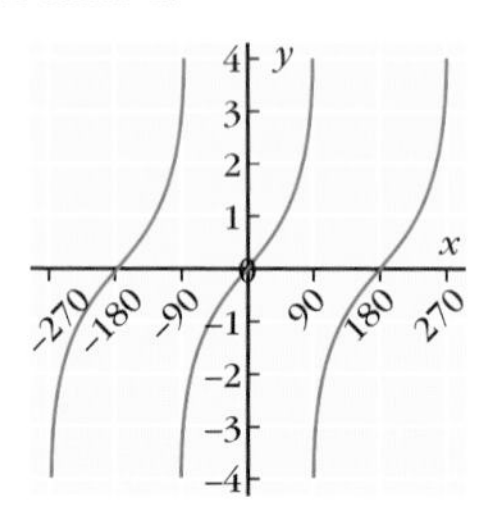

A3 $\sin x$ will be 0.5 or –0.5, so the other solutions are 150°, 210° and 330°.

A4 $\tan x$ has to be –0.5, so the only other solution is 172.9° + 180° = 352.9°.

examiner's note In questions like Q3 and Q4, use the graphs of sin, cos and tan to check that you have obtained all possible solutions.

Vectors

Q1 ABC is a triangle in which $\overrightarrow{AB} = 2\mathbf{p}$ and $\overrightarrow{AC} = 2\mathbf{q}$. X is the midpoint of AC and Y is the midpoint of BC. Show that XY is parallel to AB.

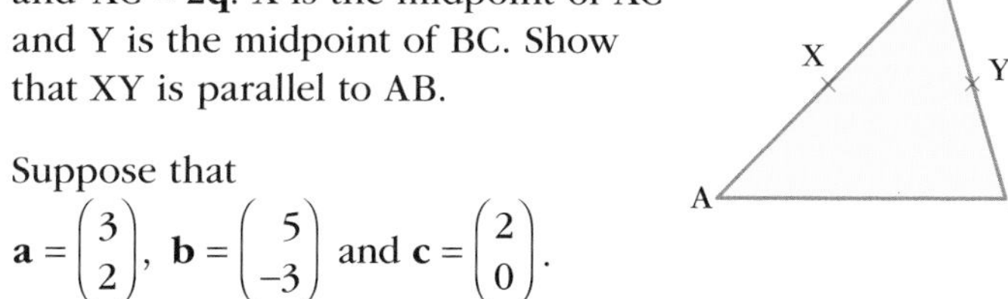

Q2 Suppose that

$$\mathbf{a} = \begin{pmatrix} 3 \\ 2 \end{pmatrix}, \ \mathbf{b} = \begin{pmatrix} 5 \\ -3 \end{pmatrix} \text{ and } \mathbf{c} = \begin{pmatrix} 2 \\ 0 \end{pmatrix}.$$

(a) Write down the vectors:

(i) $\mathbf{a} + 3\mathbf{b}$ (ii) $3\mathbf{a} - 2\mathbf{b} + 4\mathbf{c}$

(b) Find integers m and n for which the vector $m\mathbf{a} + n\mathbf{b}$ is parallel to $\mathbf{c}$.

ANSWERS

A1 $\overrightarrow{BC} = \overrightarrow{BA} + \overrightarrow{AC} = -2\mathbf{p} + 2\mathbf{q}$ and $\overrightarrow{BY} = \frac{1}{2}\overrightarrow{BC} = -\mathbf{p} + \mathbf{q}$

$\overrightarrow{XY} = \overrightarrow{XA} + \overrightarrow{AB} + \overrightarrow{BY} = -\mathbf{q} + 2\mathbf{p} + (-\mathbf{p} + \mathbf{q}) = \mathbf{p} = \frac{1}{2}\overrightarrow{AB}$,

so XY is parallel to AB.

A2 (a) (i) $\mathbf{a} + 3\mathbf{b} = \begin{pmatrix} 3 \\ 2 \end{pmatrix} + 3\begin{pmatrix} 5 \\ -3 \end{pmatrix} = \begin{pmatrix} 18 \\ -7 \end{pmatrix}$

(ii) $3\mathbf{a} - 2\mathbf{b} + 4\mathbf{c} = 3\begin{pmatrix} 3 \\ 2 \end{pmatrix} - 2\begin{pmatrix} 5 \\ -3 \end{pmatrix} + 4\begin{pmatrix} 2 \\ 0 \end{pmatrix} = \begin{pmatrix} 7 \\ 12 \end{pmatrix}$

(b) $m\mathbf{a} + n\mathbf{b} = m\begin{pmatrix} 3 \\ 2 \end{pmatrix} + n\begin{pmatrix} 5 \\ -3 \end{pmatrix} = \begin{pmatrix} 3m + 5n \\ 2m - 3n \end{pmatrix}$

$\mathbf{c}$ has no y component, so we want m and n such that $m\mathbf{a} + n\mathbf{b}$ has no y component, i.e. $2m - 3n = 0$. The integers $m = 3$ and $n = 2$ will do.

examiner's note Be especially careful with negative signs when working with vectors — often the different components have different signs.

Averages I

Q1 Find the mean of 7, 9, 14, 15, 20.

Q2 Find the mean of:

x	5	6	7	8
f	4	7	5	4

Q3 Find the mean of:

x	30–39	40–49	50–59	60–69
f	3	4	2	1

ANSWERS

A1 sum = $7 + 9 + 14 + 15 + 20 = 65$
mean = $65 \div 5 = 13$

A2 $\Sigma xf = 5 \times 4 + 6 \times 7 + 7 \times 5 + 8 \times 4 = 20 + 42 + 35 + 32 = 129$
$\Sigma f = 4 + 7 + 5 + 4 = 20$, so mean = $129 \div 20 = 6.45$

A3 From grouped frequency data it is only possible to calculate an estimate of the mean, by taking the midpoint of each interval as an estimate for the average value of the observations in that interval. Here the midpoints of the intervals are at 34.5, 44.5, 54.5 and 64.5.

Estimate of the sum = Σmf
$= 34.5 \times 3 + 44.5 \times 4 + 54.5 \times 2 + 64.5 \times 1 = 455$

$\Sigma f = 3 + 4 + 2 + 1 = 10$,
so estimate of the mean = $455 \div 10 = 45.5$

examiner's note The mean is the type of 'average' that is usually intended, unless the question specifies otherwise.

Averages II

Q1 Find the median, mode and range of:

(a) 9, 14, 20, 15, 7

(b) 6, 9, 10, 10, 11, 12, 14, 16

Q2

x	30–39	40–49	50–59	60–69
f	3	4	2	1

(a) State the interval in which the median lies.

(b) State the modal group.

(c) What is the maximum possible range of this set of data?

ANSWERS

A1 (a) In ascending order the data are 7, 9, 14, 15, 20. So the median is 14 (the middle number). There is no mode. The range is $20 - 7 = 13$.

(b) The median is the average of the two middle values, 10 and 11, so the median is 10.5. The mode is 10 because it occurs the most often, and the range is $16 - 6 = 10$.

A2 (a) There are $3 + 4 + 2 + 1 = 10$ values, so the median is the average of the 5th and 6th values, both of which lie in the 40–49 interval.

(b) The modal group is 40–49 since it contains more values (4) than any other group.

(c) The highest possible value is 69 and the lowest is 30, so the maximum possible range is 39.

***examiner's* note** The mean and the median do not have to be values that appear in the data set. If the mean turns out to be, say 3.259…, you should round it to 3.3 rather than an integer value if the problem has not asked for a particular accuracy.

Combining means

Q1 The times taken by a group of five boys to complete a mini-sudoku puzzle were (in seconds): 32, 45, 37, 49, 47

(a) Calculate the mean time taken by the boys.

A group of ten girls completed the same puzzle. Their mean time was 48 seconds.

(b) Calculate the mean time taken for the whole group.

Q2 Explain why the overall mean when two groups of data are combined will not normally be the same as the average of the means of the two groups. When will it be the same?

ANSWERS

A1 (a) mean = $(32 + 45 + 37 + 49 + 47) \div 5 = 210 \div 5 = 42$

(b) The total time for the ten girls was $48 \times 10 = 480$ seconds, and the total time for the 15 people in the combined group is $210 + 480 = 690$ seconds, so the overall mean for the combined group is $690 \div 15 = 46$ seconds.

A2 The mean of the combined group will be weighted according to the size of the two groups, so the overall mean will be closer to the mean of the larger group (e.g. in Q1 the overall mean of 46 is closer to the girls' mean of 48 than to the boys' mean of 42). The overall mean will be equal to the average of the two means if the groups are of equal size.

examiner's note Remember that you can calculate the total for any group if you know the mean and the number of people in the group.

Measures of spread

Q1 The times between eruptions of the Old Faithful Geyser have median 75 minutes, lower quartile 60 minutes and upper quartile 81 minutes. Another geyser has a median time between eruptions of 24 minutes, with an interquartile range of 44 minutes.

(a) Compare the times between eruptions of the two geysers.

(b) Why do you think the Old Faithful got its name?

Q2 Lance measured the heights of six plants. The median height was 27 cm. The range of the heights was 9 cm. Lance worked out the mean height to be 16 cm. Explain why he **must** be wrong.

ANSWERS

A1 (a) On average there is a much longer interval between eruptions of the Old Faithful than the other geyser, and the lower interquartile range (21 minutes compared to 44 minutes) means that the intervals for the Old Faithful are much more consistent in length than those of the other geyser.

(b) It got its name from the reliability of its eruptions — park rangers can predict reasonably well for tourists when the next eruption will be.

A2 If the median is 27, then at least three of the six plants must be at least 27 cm tall. Since the range is only 9 cm, none of the plants can be shorter than 18 cm, so it is not possible for the mean to be 16 cm.

examiner's note Q2 requires watertight logic to prove that it is not possible for the mean to be 16 cm. In problems like this, it is not enough to just show that you haven't been able to find a set of values that work; there will always be sufficient information provided for you to identify the 'most extreme case', which will supply the proof.

Bar charts

Q1 The number of bronze certificates awarded in the Junior UK Maths Challenge in a school were 4 from Year 7, 11 from Year 8 and 17 from Year 9. Draw a bar chart to show this information.

Q2 The bar chart shows the number of pupils from Years 10 and 11 gaining different levels of award in the Intermediate maths challenge. Compare the performance of the two year groups.

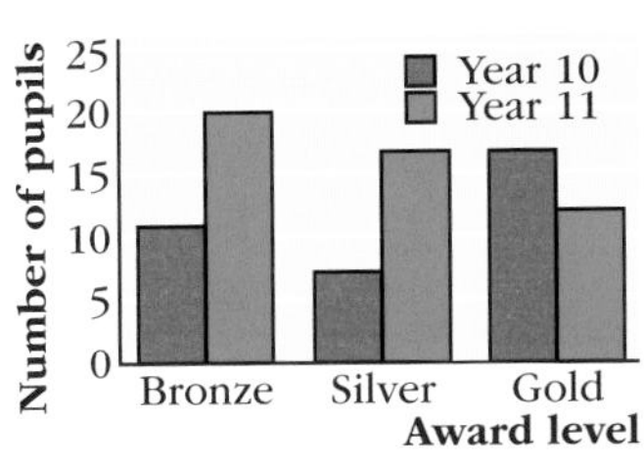

Intermediate UK Maths Challenge

A1

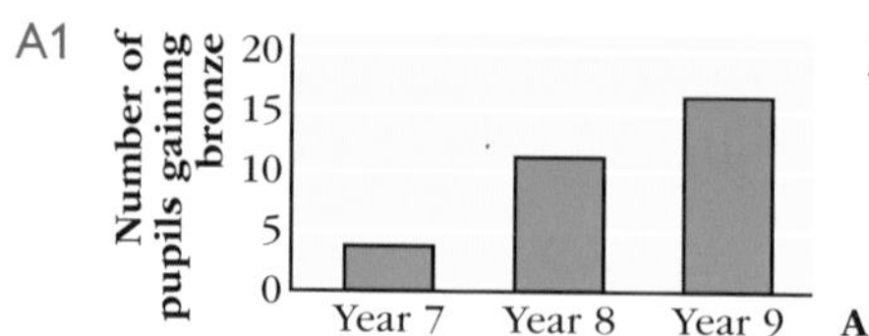

Junior UK Maths Challenge

A2 More pupils in Year 11 got awards of some sort than from Year 10 (49 compared with 36), but a much higher proportion of the awards to Year 10 pupils were gold, and Year 10 got more golds than did Year 11. It could be that Year 11 has greater strength in terms of depth of mathematical understanding, but Year 10 has more really good pupils; however, this assumes a consistent approach to entering the competition from the two year groups.

examiner's note When interpreting a graph, you need to be careful to offer a reason for why a particular pattern in the data has occurred — there is often more than one possible explanation.

Pie charts

Q1 Draw a pie chart for the following data, which represent the team supported at a particular sporting event:

	Home team	Away team	Neutral
Number of people	37 385	12 640	5393

Q2 In the pie chart shown, 12 people passed their driving test at the first attempt.

(a) How many people are represented in the pie chart altogether?

(b) Estimate the number of people who passed at the third attempt.

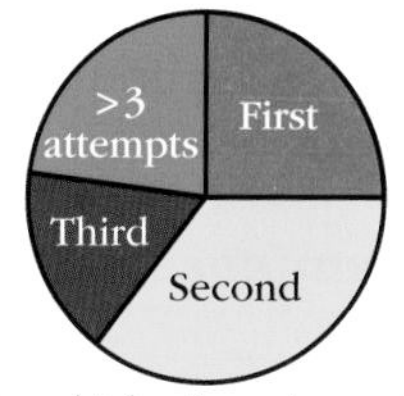

On which attempt people passed their driving test

ANSWERS

A1 The total crowd size is 55 418, so the angle for each group is found by dividing the number in the group by 55 418 and multiplying by 360°, giving angles of 243°, 82° and 35°.

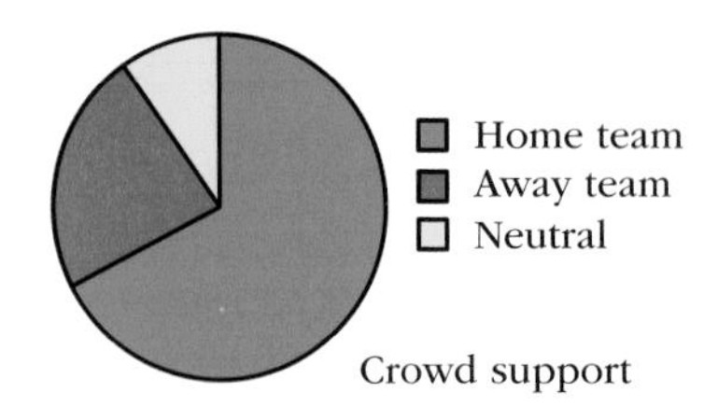

A2 (a) The group with 12 members in it accounts for $\frac{1}{4}$ of the pie chart, so there are 48 people altogether.

(b) The group of people who passed at the third attempt has an angle of 60°, so there are $60°/360° \times 48 = 8$ of them.

examiner's note Be sure to provide a key for each pie chart.

Stem and leaf diagrams

Q1 The following stem and leaf diagram shows the number of minor mistakes made on driving tests marked by a particular examiner.

Stem	Leaves
0	1 4
0	5 7 7
1	0 0 1 2 3 3 4 4
1	6 7 8 8
2	0 1

1 | 6 means 16 minor mistakes

Find the median and the range of the number of mistakes recorded by this examiner.

ANSWERS

A1 There are 19 tests summarised in this stem and leaf diagram so the median is the 10th value in the list, i.e. the median is 13 minor mistakes. The range is 21 − 1 = 20 mistakes.

Stem	Leaves
0	1 4
0	5 7 7
1	0 0 1 2 3 3 4 4
1	6 7 8 8
2	0 1

1 | 6 means 16 minor mistakes

***examiner's* note** When comparing distributions, look at both the centre (median) and the spread of the data.

Boxplots

Q1 A psychologist claims to have found a method of training young people to improve their memory. She gives a memory test to a group at the start of training and another at the end. The scores of the group on the two tests are shown in the boxplots below.

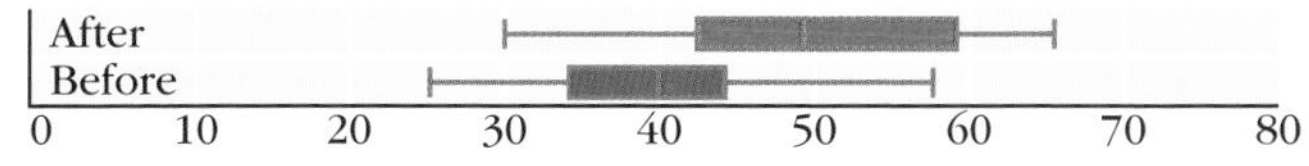

(a) Compare the performance of the group before and after the training.

(b) The psychologist claims that these results prove her method is successful. Comment on her claim.

ANSWERS

A1 (a) The two sets of data have a broadly similar shape of distribution and spread; the main difference is that the scores at all the quartiles have increased by between 5 and 10 points after training.

(b) Certainly the scores have improved for this group between the two tests, but we cannot be sure that the training is the cause of improvement; for example, gaining familiarity with the testing process could result in an improvement of test scores even without training. Also, the psychologist is claiming that the training will improve memory generally, but we do not know how large the group was, and whether they are representative of the population in general.

examiner's note Boxplots do not display the detail of the data, so concentrate on describing the main features of the distribution.

Histograms

Q1 The ages of people admitted to a hospital after a heart attack are summarised in the following table. Draw a histogram to represent this information.

Age (x years)	30–54	55–59	60–64	65–74
Number of patients	5	11	14	16

ANSWERS

A1 The interval widths are 15, 5, 5 and 10 years, so the frequency densities are 0.33, 2.2, 2.8 and 1.6.

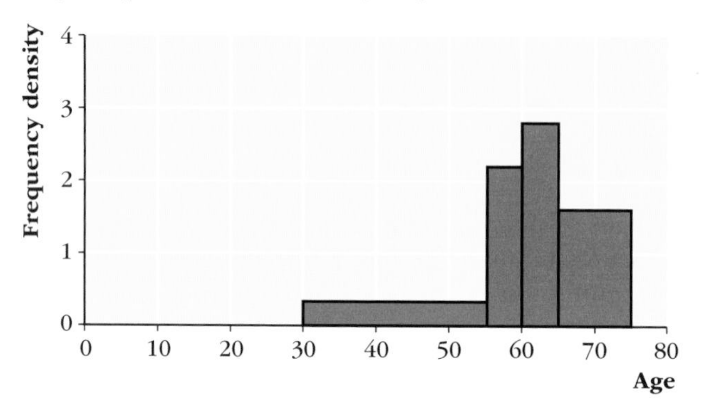

examiner's note Histograms show the average rate of occurrence in each interval.

Cumulative frequency diagrams

Q1 The cumulative frequency curve below shows the lengths of marrows grown by a gardener.

(a) Estimate the median and the interquartile range of the marrow lengths.

(b) Draw a boxplot to show the lengths of the marrows.

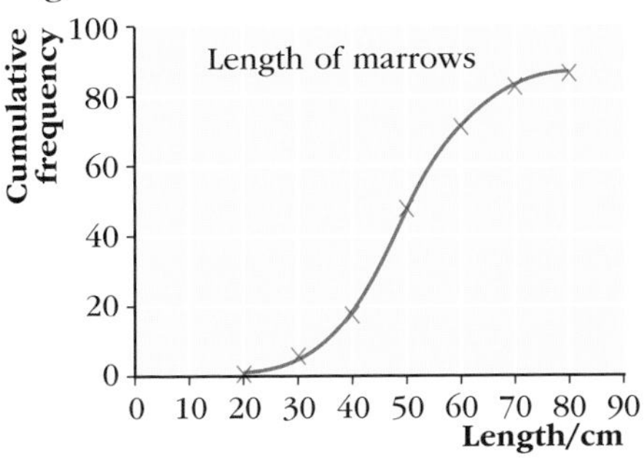

ANSWERS

A1 (a) There are 85 marrows altogether, so the median is at 43 (or 42.5), where the estimated length is 49 (or 48) cm, the lower and upper quartiles come from 21 and 63 on the cumulative frequency axis, giving estimates of around 42 and 56; thus the interquartile range is about 14.

(b)

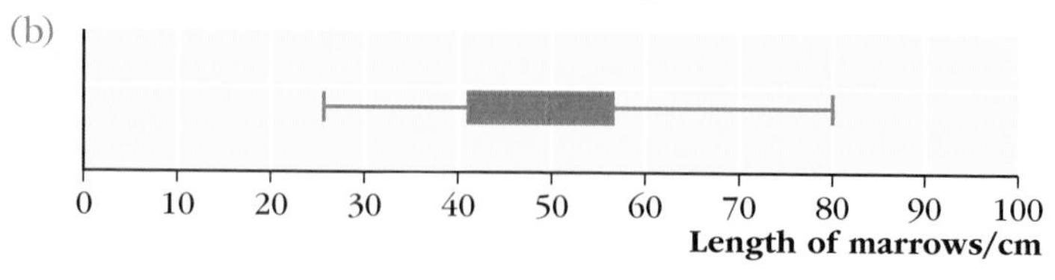

examiner's note You do not need to worry about reading, say, 42.5 or 43 very accurately on a cumulative frequency scale; however, you should always mark your graph to show where you have taken your values from.

Scatter diagrams

Q1 (a) Describe the **correlation** between the number of people vaccinated in a group and the number who catch the disease (each group has 100 people).

(b) Another group of the same size had 52 people vaccinated. Use the line of best fit to estimate the number of people catching the disease in this group.

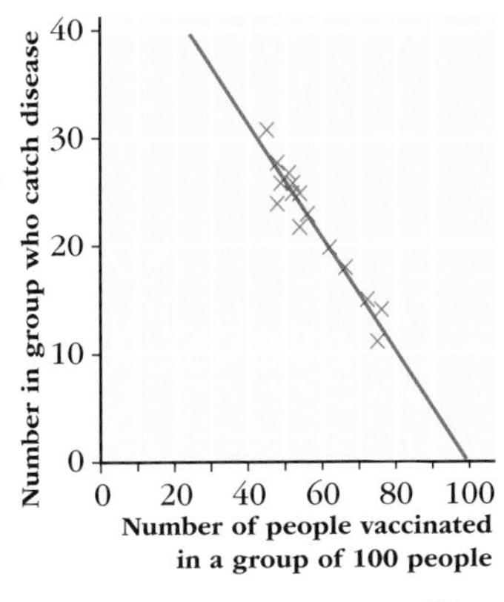

A1 (a) There is strong negative correlation between the number of people vaccinated in each group of 100 and the number catching the disease, i.e. when a larger proportion of people are vaccinated there tends to be fewer people catching the disease.

(b) 25, from the diagram below.

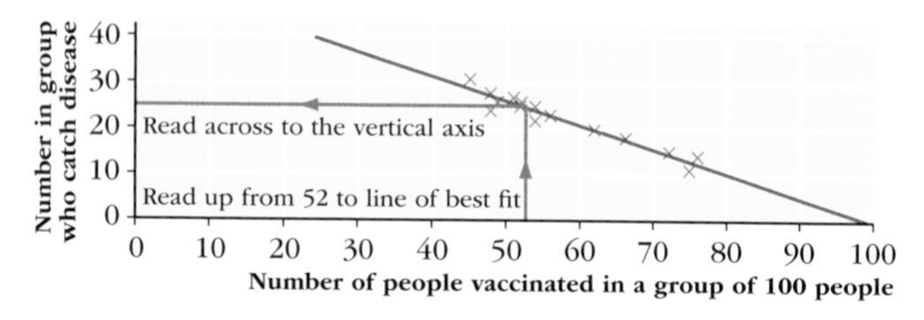

examiner's note Remember to show your working by drawing lines on the graph.

Line graphs

Q1 The table shows the number of new businesses in the manufacturing and services sectors that opened in a town in the even years over a 20-year period.

	1988	90	92	94	96	98	2000	02	04	06	08
Manufacturing	12	13	11	12	12	13	10	8	5	4	5
Services	4	6	7	7	9	10	14	13	15	14	16

(a) Plot these data as line graphs on the same axes.

(b) Compare and contrast what is happening in the two sectors.

ANSWERS

A1 (a)

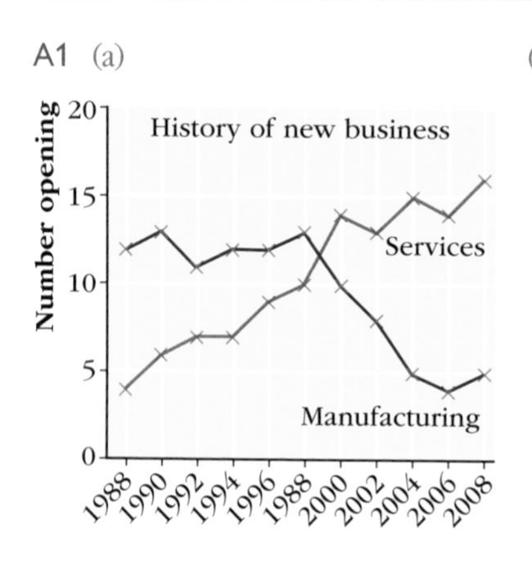

(b) The number of new businesses in the services sector has steadily increased over the 20-year period, while the number of new businesses in manufacturing dropped dramatically between 1998 and 2004. The number of businesses opening in the services sector is much higher at the end of the period than in manufacturing, whereas it was much lower at the start.

***examiner's* note** When making comparisons it is important to describe the changes qualitatively, rather than just quoting numbers.

Designing a statistical investigation

Q1 Amir is concerned about the traffic passing his house.

(a) He spends an hour one morning counting the cars going past his house. What sort of data is this?

(b) He finds that the council has installed a sensor that automatically detects when a car goes past. What is this process called?

(c) Amir gets a summary of the traffic in the past 6 months from the council. What sort of data is this?

Q2 The only information Amir has is on the number of cars. Advise him of other data he might collect if he wants to make a case to the council that the road is dangerous.

ANSWERS

A1 (a) **Primary** data because Amir collects it himself. Counts of the number of vehicles constitute **quantitative** and **discrete** data.

(b) **Data logging**.

(c) **Secondary** data because someone else did the data collection. Amir might use the data as it was collected, or after it has gone through some analysis or summarising, but it is still secondary data.

A2 Other factors that might make the road dangerous include the speed at which cars are driven at that point in the road or a difficult corner. Collecting data on car speeds and accident history on that stretch of road would provide a fuller picture.

examiner's note At the design stage it is important to think through all the questions you might want to find answers to, to ensure that all the necessary data will be collected.

Designing a record sheet

Q1 Luisella wants to compare the amount of advertising that appears in four daily newspapers.

(a) Design a record sheet to help her.

To save time, she decides to look only at the first six and last six pages of each paper.

(b) Explain why this is a bad idea, and suggest a better way of choosing 12 pages to look at.

ANSWERS

A1 (a) Record the proportion of space taken by adverts on each page in each paper:

	Paper			
Page	**1**	**2**	**3**	**4**
1				
2				
3				
⋮				

This is only an example; an alternative method would be to simply count the total number of ads in each paper.

(b) In most newspapers, the first few pages are news and the back few pages are sports, so the pages Luisella is choosing are probably unrepresentative of the overall amount of advertising. Choose pages randomly or by a stratified sampling method.

examiner's note Common sense is important in identifying fair ways to take samples; take care to explain clearly the reasons underlying your method.

Questionnaire design

Q1 A newspaper plans to conduct a survey about parole for violent crimes and has the following question in the draft questionnaire:

'Prisoners convicted of violent crimes should automatically be eligible for parole after they have served what proportion of their sentences?'

The options given in the draft are:

0 to $\frac{1}{3}$ $\quad\quad$ $\frac{1}{2}$ to $\frac{2}{3}$ $\quad\quad$ $\frac{3}{4}$ $\quad\quad$ no automatic right

Suggest some better options.

ANSWERS

A1 The questionnaire designer can decide where the cutoffs for the options should be, but it is essential that there be no gaps. Generally a choice of four or five options is reasonable. So a better set of options might be:

up to $\frac{1}{3}$ from $\frac{1}{3}$ to $\frac{2}{3}$ over $\frac{2}{3}$ no automatic right

examiner's note Options need to be distinct and must cover all possible values, so that every response will fit into exactly one option.

Probability I

Q1 Bag A contains four red, two blue and six black discs. One disc is chosen at random from the bag.

(a) What is the probability that the disc is blue?

(b) What is the probability that the disc is not red?

(c) Four hundred people each take a disc out and immediately return it to the bag. How many people would you expect to take out a blue disc?

Q2 A spinner has three coloured sections. Ahmed estimates the probabilities of the spinner landing on each of the colours as 0.38 for red, 0.41 for blue and 0.31 for yellow. Explain why these estimates cannot all be correct.

ANSWERS

A1 (a) There are 12 discs altogether. P(blue) $= \frac{2}{12} = \frac{1}{6}$

(b) P(red) $= \frac{4}{12} = \frac{1}{3}$, so P(not red) $= \frac{2}{3}$

or calculate directly that there are 8 discs which are not red, and $\frac{8}{12} = \frac{2}{3}$

(c) The proportion is likely to be close to the probability of getting a blue on any go, so it is about

$\frac{1}{6} \times 400 = 66.7$ (i.e. 67 people).

A2 The total probability must always come to 1, but $0.38 + 0.41 + 0.31 = 1.1$, so these estimates cannot all be correct.

examiner's note Unless you are very secure in your arithmetical work with fractions, it is worth first writing down each probability as a fraction of numbers as they are given in the question, e.g. as $\frac{2}{12}$, and then simplifying later on in the problem.

Probability II

Q1 A fair die is used in a game where you have to throw more than a two to make a move.

(a) If I have 14 throws in a game, how many moves am I likely to be able to make?

(b) Suzanne makes only five moves in her first ten throws of a game. Is she justified in complaining that the die must not be fair?

ANSWERS

A1 (a) I can move if I throw a three, four, five or six, so the probability of being able to move is $\frac{2}{3}$ on any throw. On average I will be able to move $\frac{2}{3} \times 14 = 9.33$ times, i.e. I am likely to be able to move nine or ten times.

(b) On average, in ten throws one would expect to move $\frac{2}{3} \times 10$ times, i.e. six or seven times. While Suzanne has moved only five times, this is not particularly unusual (and neither would moving eight or nine or even four times in ten throws). She would need a lot more evidence that she was moving consistently less than two-thirds of her throws before a complaint could be taken seriously.

***examiner's* note** With only a small number of trials, it is hard to draw a conclusion that an unusual result is not just a random event.

Probability III

Q1 A bag contains six red and four black balls. Two balls are taken out without replacement.

(a) Draw a tree diagram to represent this situation.

(b) What is the probability that two red balls are drawn.

(c) Which of the following is most likely?

two reds
two blacks
a red and a black

(d) If two balls of the same colour are taken out, what is the probability that they are black?

ANSWERS

A1 (a)

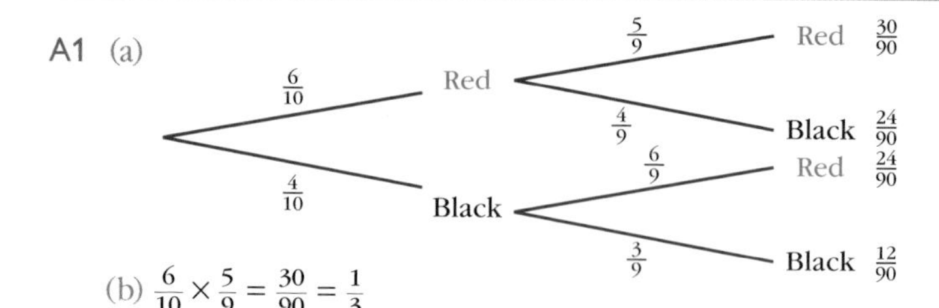

(b) $\frac{6}{10} \times \frac{5}{9} = \frac{30}{90} = \frac{1}{3}$

(c) P(two reds) $= \frac{30}{90}$, P(two blacks) $= \frac{12}{90}$

and P(a red and a black) $= \frac{24}{90} + \frac{24}{90} = \frac{48}{90}$,

so a red and a black is the most likely.

(d) P(both red) $= \frac{30}{90}$ and P(both black) $= \frac{12}{90}$,

so P(both black | same colour) $= \dfrac{\frac{12}{90}}{\frac{12}{90} + \frac{30}{90}} = \frac{12}{42} = \frac{2}{7}$

***examiner's* note** Keeping a common denominator for all probabilities at any stage, and simplifying only at the end, will make the working much easier than if you simplified each probability earlier.

Probability IV

Q1 The table shows the number of students on the maths course at a certain university.

	Year 1	Year 2	Year 3	Total
Males	62	59	52	**173**
Females	83	56	63	**202**
Total	**145**	**115**	**115**	**375**

Find the probability that:

(a) a student chosen at random from the first year is male

(b) a student chosen at random is a female from the second year

(c) a female chosen at random is from the second year

(d) a student chosen at random is from the third year

A1 (a) $\frac{62}{145}$

(b) $\frac{56}{375}$

(c) $\frac{56}{202}$

(d) $\frac{115}{375}$

examiner's note Be careful in identifying the group from which the selection is made; for example, in Q1(a) it comprises all the first-year students, and in Q1(c) it consists of all the female students.

Sampling methods I

Q1 (a) Explain the difference between a census and a sample.
(b) Give two reasons why sampling is used.

Q2 A die is thrown repeatedly and a random sample of 60 scores is recorded. There are eight sixes in the sample. Comment on the following statements:
(a) The sample is biased because there should be ten sixes.
(b) The die is biased because there should be ten sixes.

Q3 A survey is undertaken to find out the proportions of people who are unemployed, in part-time work or in full-time work. Explain why asking people in a town centre at 11 a.m. is not a good idea.

ANSWERS

A1 (a) A census encompasses the whole population, whereas a sample is a subset of the whole population.

(b) It would often be too expensive or time-consuming to take a census, and in some cases it is impossible.

A2 (a) An individual sample cannot be biased; it is the sampling method that could be biased.

(b) Getting eight sixes in 60 throws is not particularly unusual — on average, with a fair die, there should be ten sixes; however, individual samples will often give 12 or 13, perhaps six or seven, and maybe other numbers of sixes — this would not be sufficiently convincing evidence of the die being biased.

A3 People in full-time work are likely to be at work at 11 a.m.; therefore they would be under-represented in the sample.

examiner's note Small samples are not good because they do not give stable outcomes — two different small samples could tell very different stories.

Sampling methods II

Q1 The table below shows the numbers of boys and girls in a sixth-form college. The principal wants to conduct a survey of 50 pupils to find out views on new rules introduced for the study areas. How many pupils should he take from each group?

	Year 12	**Year 13**
Boys	113	117
Girls	108	126

ANSWERS

A1 There are 464 pupils altogether, so we want to take $\frac{50}{464}$ of each group; this does not come out evenly, so we round to the nearest whole number, giving 12 boys from year 12, 13 boys from year 13, 12 girls from year 12 and 14 girls from year 13. However, these numbers total 51, so one of the values that has been rounded up needs to be rounded down instead: we note that the value for year 13 girls was closest to the 0.5 cut-off for rounding, so 13 girls should be taken from year 13.

examiner's note The key to determining whether stratified sampling is better than simple random sampling in a given situation is to think whether you can identify groups which might be expected to give different outcomes for whatever it is you are investigating.